God's Free-Man

An American Tale of Perseverance:
A Life in Service

BY TED FREEMAN

DORRANCE
PUBLISHING CO
EST. 1920
PITTSBURGH, PENNSYLVANIA 15238

Dorrance Publishing Co
585 Alpha Drive
Pittsburgh, PA 15238
Visit our website at www.dorrancebookstore.com

ISBN: 978-1-6491-3341-0
eISBN: 978-1-6491-3590-2

This book is the Father's work. I worked only as his scribe, so that what God wanted is made abundantly known and would be done at this time. I humbly, with great servitude to our Father, present God's work for us.

—-Pastor Ted

Contents

Thank you to my daughter Nyree Freeman-Williamson and my brother Dr. Joseph Freeman, whose research made it possible for me to complete this project. Thank you to Ethel Freeman-Shabazz for being a rock of support. Thank you to my son Corey Salaam for keeping "Pops" focused, and to my North Star and Pillar of Love, Direction and Comfort my wife Rhonda L Freeman, I Love You!!!

Author's Notes

It has taken me fifty-two years to achieve permission to write this work. I have learned to come in line with Obedience to God's Will for my life. While stumbling and growing every day of my life, The Great "I Am" showing me his Grace and Mercy has allowed me to put to pen with clarity the history of how God has shown the Freeman Family favor in the midst of that living nightmare known as slavery and general life.

Like the patriarchs and people of the Bible, we have constantly strayed from the path that God had prepared for us and took our giftings into the world. We find creative and not so creative ways to destroy ourselves and others. Despite our disobedience God has always kept open an exit ramp for us to get back to Him.

Masego and Rehema were captive slaves in Africa. They were set free by God in the middle of the Atlantic

Ocean, never to be slaves on land again. What I have discovered is that the Freeman Clan is a perfect representation of every family ever created by God. We are saved only by the Grace and Mercy of our Heavenly Father.

Your "pride" wants to shout, "I'm free!" The reality is that freedom only comes by submitting to God's Will for your life. There is nothing worse than a "Free-Man or Free-Woman" who is enslaved Spiritually.

All references, empirical and inclusionary information in this writing were given by the Lord over the past fifty-two years. I will not attempt to cliff note this experience by adding ancillary information on this presentation.

Enjoy your read and learn a microcosm of American history that has been historically under reported but even more important enjoy how God is always there no matter what you've done or what has been done to you.

Pastor Ted

Preface

Ancient of Days

"Therefore I, a prisoner for serving the Lord, beg you to lead a life worthy of your calling, for you have been called by God. Always be humble and gentle. Be patient with each other, making allowance for each other's faults because of your love. Make every effort to keep yourselves united in the Spirit, binding yourselves together with peace."

(Ephesians 4:1-3, NLT)

Current of Days

"What then shall we say to this? If God is for us, who can be against us?"

(Romans 8:31, NAB)

This could have been the motto of the early Freeman's from the moment they were stolen from their peaceful African village even to the present day. This is their story from the 1760s to the 1930s. As you read, you will glimpse fragments from the stories passed down to you by your own ancestors; however, the Freeman story is also unique. Very few people aided Harriet Tubman both during her slave-saving days and after her stint as a soldier during the Civil War. I urge you to take this journey with this family. You will enter curious and leave wanting more.

Rhonda Freeman

1

Nchi ya Mama (The Motherland)

Conflict, War, Tension—this was the vicious cycle Masego (Ma-say-go) found himself in. Masego had just taken a new bride named Rehema (Rah-he-ma), and she was the woman he had been praying to receive from God since he was a young herdboy of eight years old. All he ever dreamed of, while grazing and protecting the cattle, was finding a loving mate, raising a family, tending his cattle, and living peacefully within his Bantu Clan, the Beti-Pahuin (Bet-tee-foo-hoom).

Masego thought he had found his perfect counterpart when he was nine years old, a young girl named Uzochi (You-zo-she). Uzochi was a young girl with a smile that started in her soul and could light up the darkest night. For Masego, her smile was paralyzing; it was like one of the bush animals staring at the flare of the torch during a night hunt. Uzochi possessed everything he wanted in a companion, a wife, and the mother of his children. She was the complete compliment to him.

Tending and protecting the family's livestock became even more important to him once he was smitten by Uzochi's charm. He knew that once he had passed into manhood he would have to have a suitable dowry to present to Uzochi's family. Masego knew he would be confronted with mounting competition from other young men for Uzochi's hand. That did not worry him; nobody was going to outwork him for the girl he loved. He knew that with the directions of God and devoting himself to his task, Uzochi would be his wife.

What was extremely special about Uzochi, besides captivating Masego with her smile and that special twinkle in her eyes, was that she was extremely unassuming, coated with an inner glow of peace. Unfortunately, misunderstanding of her given nature made her the envy of many of the girls her age. Masego was sure she would be the perfect helpmate, mother, and confidante; he knew he would have to work hard to secure their future together.

Masego stayed mindful of any ornate flowers he could bring Uzochi from his stints of managing the livestock, particularly when taking the cattle to graze. Their conversations were awkward and difficult for ten-year-olds, especially for a super shy and confused herdboy. While being in love did spark confusion in the young herdboy, the foundation of his confusion was much deeper.

Masego's confusion centered on people and what they professed as the right way and how their actions contradicted their professed beliefs. He understood why the lions, hyenas, and wild dogs did as they did. They killed to eat or protect. He understood the turf issues of water buffaloes and hippos that had killed family members and friends. They trusted nothing and were best to just avoid. He understood the dangers of going into the deep bush country and the great possibilities of injury or death. He was prepared, willing, and quite capable of addressing those issues, day or night. What created his confusion were human beings.

Why would a man with sixty head of cattle want to take the only two head of cattle that another man possesses? Why would one clan covet the possessions of another clan? Why does war and death prevail over peace and happiness? Masego did not have the answers but was continuously exposed to the cause of his personal confusion, Chief Apunda (Ah-pun-da). Chief Apunda, a Gbana (Gaw-baw-na) Noble of the Temne (Tem-nay) People of the Kingdom of Koya despised the Beti-Pahuin Clan. Their hatred of Masego's clan was deep, without explanation.

Chief Apunda was taught by his father, who was taught by his father, who was taught by his father that "the only good Beti-Pahuin is a dead Beti-Pahuin." Their hatred was not based on an event or act of aggression but on an envy based on the Beti-Pahuins' peace, happiness, and prosperity. Apunda's greed kept tensions high and the Beti-Pahuins always primed for conflict. As unfounded as this relationship between the two clans was, it's what existed, and the reality was Masego always had to be alert around them.

Chief Apunda had harassed and raided the Beti-Pahuins often. Pillaging and taking always with Masego and Beti-Pahuin warriors running them down and making them pay for their deeds. Apunda and his clan coveted their land but could never force or scare the Beti-Pahuins into abandoning their home.

One evening when Masego was close to fifteen years old, Chief Apunda attacked the Beti-Pahuins. Apunda's attack was more vicious then Masego had ever witnessed before. Usually it was a sneak attack to steal livestock or grain from the storehouses. This attack was different; he was assaulting the Beti-Pahuins. Apunda had centered his attacks on the outer huts and was taking people as prisoners instead of stealing from the cattle pens and grain huts. He also had an element of a supporting cast that the Beti-Pahuins and Masego had never seen before. There were Futa Watu, Clear People, with Chief Apunda!

Clear People (Futa Watu) had no color to their skin and their hair did not curl to protect from the sun. They were known to carry strange weapons that made thunder, and they were known to take people away, never to be seen again. The elders had told children stories about Clear People since time immemorial, but they had never been seen in the lands of the Beti-Pahuins.

Chibueze (She-boo-zee), the Chief of the Beti-Pahuin People, had seen the Clear People as a youth and knew firsthand what Clear People could do to a peaceful clan. As a small boy he was visiting, with his parents, a distant relative name Oluchi (Oh-lew-she) in the Ndowe (Dah-way) Clan. The Clear People attacked in the middle of the night, with the help of a local chieftain named Oni (Oh-knee). Thirty people were taken captive that night, including Chibueze and his father.

Chibueze's mother Adisa (Ah-dee-zah) had escaped by hiding in the thick thorny bush of the jungle. For two days and three nights Adisa followed the captives. It was the season of rain and storms, and all Adisa had for protection from the weather were banana leaves, but her husband Kamau (Ka-mah-you) and her son Chibueze had even less. On the third night, Adisa creeped into the camp of the Clear People and cut the binds that held Kamau and Chibueze. Startled by his mother's attempt to free him, Chibueze jumped and was gashed by his mother's knife.

Kamau and his family, after escaping Chief Oni and the Clear People's camp, hid in the jungle for three days, surrounded by swamps with biting insects and dangerous animals of all sorts. The Clear People were not adept at venturing into such a treacherous terrain, but Chief Oni's warriors took on the challenge. The ferocity of the storms became too great and the hazards of the jungle were too dangerous, forcing them to return to the encampment.

Adisa had saved her family from peril, and it took them ten days to return home. Kamau and his family were happy to be home but forced to have the vision of the Clear People burned into their memories. Chibueze even had a more visual and constant reminder of the ordeal, a three-inch scar on his wrist caused by Adisa cutting his bonds.

The night that Chief Apunda and the Clear People attacked the Beti-Pahuins, chaos ruled; seventeen members of the Beti-Pahuin Clan were taken, among them taken was Uzochi!

Uzochi fought and screamed, but she was no match for Apunda's warriors. Masego ran to her screams but was intercepted by several assailants. He fought bravely and dispatched three of Apunda's warriors but was hurt in the melee and could not immediately catchup to Uzochi. She was gone!

Masego and a small company of warriors tracked them for three days until they reached the Mbeya (May-yah) River to no avail. Uzochi was gone forever.

Uzochi and the other sixteen members of the clan, mothers, fathers, sisters, brothers, daughters, and sons taken were never to be seen again. Masego was heartbroken, the love of his life taken from him for no visible reason, just taken!

Masego's life slipped into a fog of despair. For the next three years he carried out his duties, kept his faith in God but had lost the zest to his personality. This worried his mother Femi (Fam-e), but all she could do was pray. He dreamt about what would have been important in his life and how those dreams had been completely destroyed, never to come to realization. He had no interest in a relationship with the Beti-Pahuin women he had grown up around. They only reminded him of Uzochi and what could never be.

One day Chibueze, chief of the Beti-Pahuin Clan, sent Masego on a diplomatic mission to Chief Zuberi (Zoo-mari) of the Bubi (Boo-be) Clan. Chibueze had learned that the Clear People were becoming more and more active in their region, with the support of Chief Apunda and a few other chieftains. Masego had learned on one of his spying missions for Chief Chibueze that Apunda was receiving a large commission for helping the Clear People secure individuals from surrounding Clans to be sold. Chibueze thought it was time for the Bubi People and the Beti-Pahuin People to unite and defeat Apunda and those chieftains supporting him. They must work together to end these rampages, brought on by the Clear People, Chief Apunda, and his allies.

While carrying out his diplomatic mission with Chief Zuberi of the Bubi Clan, Masego was invited to a feast in his honor. Masego had no interest in festive occasions, but this was part of his diplomatic responsibilities. Reluctantly he went and immediately discovered a beacon of hope. At the gathering he saw and met Rufaro (Rue-far-oh) and his daughters Mudiwa (Moo-dee-wah) and Rehema.

Masego was immediately enamored with Rehema's poise, charm, and graciousness. He was extremely elated that his diplomatic mission for Chief Chibueze was completed. He was totally smitten by Rehema and may have botched or impeded his assignment for Chief Chibueze. His work was done, and he spent the evening talking to Rehema about whatever popped into their heads.

Rehema seemed enthralled with this young man. Strong, kind, intelligent, well-spoken with a smile that could melt shea butter; this was the man she had been looking for her entire life. In her mind, she was not going to lose this opportunity to explore becoming complete.

Masego, after having a great time at the banquet, was feeling something that had been absent in his life for years, love. He was falling in love with Rehema, but his sensation of euphoria turned immediately into guilt. Guilt that was being driven by Masego's culpability in abandoning the memory of his love for Uzochi. How could he forsake those memories of affection that he had developed and nourished with Uzochi in order to move forward with Rehema? He realized that moving forward with Rehema meant total commitment from him in mind, body, and spirit. Masego had a quagmire of thoughts and rationales that, if not addressed, would assure an inability to enter a growing relationship with Rehema.

All night he wrestled back and forth with what he had and what was being presented to him. Torment and anguish ruled his night. Finally, after exerting all his strength and mental anguish, Masego cried out to God!

As he slumped into a state of complete weakness and submission, he heard a small, still voice that brought him clarity. It was God. Masego said, "Help me, God!" The Creator said, ***"Your hands are too full of grief to accept My Gift for you."*** Such a simple phrase that brought Masego such clarity. He was holding onto vapors of a past time. Vapors that were just like the fog after a heavy rain, hindering his vision and movements forward. If he was to move forward with his life and destiny, according to God, he would have to open his hand and let the vapors dissipate! Masego rose up out of his state of despair, washed his face, and moved with purpose to accept his Gift from God.

Sango (Sang-oh) and Isoba (Saw-bah) had accompanied Masego on his diplomatic mission to Chief Zuberi of the Bubi People. Chief Zuberi accepted and strongly endorsed all the points presented to him by Chief Chibueze of the Beti-Pahuins. He had committed the Bubi People to fight alongside the Beti-Pahuins against the atrocities of Chief Apunda and the Clear People. Now the most important task for Masego was conveying this information to Chief Chibueze.

The immediate dilemma was commitment to his duties to Chief Chibueze and his growing love for Rehema; both required his full attention. Masego knew his obligation to his clan was of greater importance, but he was determined not to lose Rehema.

Masego decided to send Sango with a detail report to Chief Chibueze outlining Chief Zuberi's agreement in all his areas of concern. He also informed Sango to inform Chief Chibueze about his desire to marry Rehema. Sango was to tell him, Masego said, "With your approval I will return with a bride." Masego told Sango that if Chibueze disapproved of the marriage, he would immediately return home. If Chief Chibueze approved, Sango was then to join Isoba and bring him the dowry for Rehema.

Masego sent Isoba to his father Unathi (You-not-thee) to secure the necessary livestock for a dowry to give to Rehema's father, Rufaro, and his family once Chibueze gave his approval. Masego also told Isoba to tell his mother Femi that he loved her and missed her. Once Sango received Chief Chibueze's approval Isoba and

Sango would bring the dowry to him. Masego gave them the specifics of what the dowry was to consist of: one young bull, one oxen, four head of cattle, four sheep, and six goats. Unathi assigned three herdboys to accompany Isoba and Sango back to Masego. Masego was not going to be outbid for the affections of Rehema.

Chief Chibueze was elated about the agreement between the Beti-Pahuin People and the Bubi People. Chief Chibueze had always found Chief Zuberi to be a very competent leader and he felt confident that they could bring this menace of Clear People and Chief Apunda to an end. When Sango told Chief Chibueze about Masego's love interest and his desire to bring Rehema home as his bride, the Chief was delighted.

Chibueze had spent the last few years trying to remedy Masego's despair. Masego had proven himself as a great warrior, a skilled diplomat, and was showing himself to be a very good administrator for the Beti-Pahuin Clan. All Chibueze could do was pray to God to help Masego. He gave permission as well as blessings to Masego and specified that Sago inform him of the day of the wedding as quickly as possible. Chibueze's permission and blessing was all Masego needed to proceed with his plans to make Rehema his wife.

While Sago and Isoba handled the business before them, Masego was advancing his plans. He made an audience before Chief Zuberi to share his intentions and to receive his permission and blessing to proceed. Chief Zuberi granted his approval and gave Masego his blessing. Next, he shared his intentions with Rufaro, Rehema's father, and sought his permission and blessing. Rufaro was pleased that such an industrious and spiritual man wanted to complete his daughter. Rufaro gave his permission and blessing with great joy.

With permissions obtained and blessings bestowed, there was only one thing left for Masego to do; he must show Rehema that he would be that man who could appreciate a woman of her quality. It was a wise decision on his part. Masego had no idea of her training and background. In his courting process he learned a valuable lesson, the impact of her mother.

Chinwe (Chin-wee) was a stately lady with dark piercing eyes. She was a kind-hearted woman who showed great reverence to God and love to anyone she came within contact. While being devoted to her husband Rufaro and loyal to Chief Zuberi and the Bubi Clan, there was something about Chinwe that made you realize that she was always three steps ahead of you on any issue, topic, or deed. She made sure this persona had been translated and transferred to her daughters Rehema and Mudiwa.

Chinwe had been an Agooji (Ah-go-gee) Warrior. She was not just a member of the most feared and dangerous all-female warrior army in Africa, but a captain of the elite "Reapers," the Wavunaji.

As a child, Chinwe had been kidnapped from her home within the Bubi Clan. King Agaja (Ah-gah-jah) of the Fon (Fawn) People, king of the Kingdom of Dahomey sent an attachment of Agooji Warriors to raid the Bubi People. Chinwe was taken along with some other young children, who were playing Achi (Ah-she).

Achi was a board game that helped herdboys develop their thinking and strategy skills. Chinwe was the only girl playing because she was the best player of Achi in her village. No herdboy could beat her at Achi. While they were playing their regular version of "Champion of the Day," the Agooji Warriors attacked! Nine children were taken, and Chinwe was the only girl. The fate of the eight boys who were taken had already been determined; they would become slaves, but the feisty young girl with the steely eyes was another matter.

The trip to Abomey, the capitol of the Kingdom of Dahomey, was very enlightening for Awiti (Wee-tee). She was the captain of the raiding party and a member of the most dangerous unit within the Agooji Army, the Wavunaji, the Reapers. Awiti had broken her command into four distinct raiding units and had captured twenty-nine Bubis, twenty-eight males and one female Chinwe.

Chinwe's gaze could not be broken; she was mad. She wasn't scared nor did she cry for her mother or father;

she was mad. It wasn't that she was mad at the Agoojis; she was mad with herself for not possessing the skills and abilities to have kept Awiti and the Agooji Warriors from accomplishing a successful raid.

Chinwe watched everything they did on the journey, including how they handled their weapons, especially the "Ndevu ya Muda Mrefu," a two-handed razor three feet long. On the way to Abomey, Chinwe saw Awiti dispatch two hyenas with two deadly slashes. The largest one was literally cut in half with one slash of the Ndevu ya Muda Mrefu. Chinwe wanted her own!

The journey to Abomey took eighteen days. The Agooji Warriors traveled only with their weapons, a gourd of water, and their grass matts. Their pace of travel was greatly impeded by the inclusion of the captives, so it was necessary to hunt on a daily basis. Chinwe had never seen "Gebetos," women hunters, before being captured. She was mad and enthralled with the variety of animals that where killed by these Gebetos.

Awiti had noticed Chinwe's interest in everything Agooji. To test her theory, she moved Chinwe closer to her mat in the evenings. This gave Chinwe the opportunity to see her tend to her weapons and see some of the ways of an Agooji Warrior. Awiti watched as Chinwe became more enthralled than mad, which led to Chinwe becoming more and more inquisitive.

2

MAFUNZO (The TRAINING)

The city of Abomey sat on top of a high plateau. Great effort had gone into making the capitol of the Kingdom of Dahomey a pleasure to the eyes. Great applause rose from the people of Abomey as the captives were paraded through the streets on their way to the Nyumba Kubwa, the Great Home of King Agaja. All captives were presented before the king before assignment. Captives with any noticeable skills or potential talent could be assigned according to Agaja's decree. It was Awiti's task to stand near the King and share the individuals' skills, talents, or possible future benefit to the Kingdom.

Chinwe was the last captive to be presented to King Agaja. Awiti spent a considerable amount of time whispering something to the king. This produced a lengthy discussion between King Agaja and his Agooji captain. Agaja paused and looked at Chinwe with a deliberate glare and said in a finite tone, "You will be an Agooji

Warrior, a protector of the Kingdom of Dahomey and the Mlinzi, the bodyguards of the King."

Chinwe started her training the next day. The Agooji philosophy was, **"YOU CAN NOT BECOME A GREAT LEADER UNTIL YOU BECOME A GREAT FOLLOWER!"**

Menial tasks around the training village combined with degrading servitude were the first level of preparation she was to endure. Presented with the elimination of her self-pride, self-worth, and the abandonment of her dignity made this phase the hardest part of training for a proud little girl.

Once she abandoned self and accepted the collective philosophy of the Agooji Code of Obedience, she was permitted to accompany them on raids and missions. Chinwe's responsibility was to transport the grass mats, utensils, and extra weapons for three warriors. Her only personal weapon was a knife. It was the only weapon she was permitted to use whether in a life threatening situation with an enemy or a wild beast. Her skills with a knife and Chinwe's dedication to caring and honing her knife were quite impressive in the eyes of Awiti.

Training continued, and Chinwe was introduced to the weapons of the Agoojis. She became proficient with the club, the spear, the rifle, and sword, but she was not permitted to touch the "Ndevu ya Muda Mrefu," the two-handed, three-foot razor which was reserved for the Reapers, the Wavunaji, the elite of the elite, the most skilled and feared warriors in Africa. Chinwe had become one of the best hunters among the Agoojis and had proven herself in combat as a fearless combatant. She had embraced the warrior's lifestyle completely.

Awiti saw her development and believed in Chinwe's acceptance of the Agooji Code of Obedience. Awiti approached the king about her joining the Wavunaji. Their discussion was thorough and emotional. King Agaja finally accepted Awiti's recommendation. Chinwe was allowed to train and became a Reaper. Chinwe became a true terror to anyone that opposed her or dared to challenge her on the battlefield. Against the Annobon (Knawbon) Clan, she led the attack party that captured King Wekesa (Wah-kay-zah), king of the Annobon People. His capture brought the Annobon Clan under submission to King Agaja and led to the inclusion of the Annobon Clan as part of the Kingdom of Dahomey. On another venture against the Igbo (E-bow) Clan, Chinwe captured a key hilly intersection with a handful of warriors that prevented the Igbos from advancing until the main body of Agooji Warriors were in position to repel the Igbos. Chinwe had her "Ndevu ya Muda Mrefu," and she used it! Venture after venture she succeeded in accomplishing the goals of the king and the Kingdom of Dahomey.

Her role as a Reaper within the Agooji Army was beginning to weigh heavily on her. The deaths she caused and the nightmares she created were eating at her inner self. She found it difficult, in her quiet times, to believe that she, Chinwe, was the architect of all this death and maiming. She pondered how that little girl playing Achi, with hope for her future, could lose her sensibility and moral direction. It was too painful and unproductive to stay in that mire of hurt, shame, and guilt brought on by her past. She remembered what she had been taught about placing her future in the past. The elders in her Bubi Village would tell her, **"Your shoulders will never be wide enough to carry your griefs and pains; give them to God."** So she did. By becoming more obedient to the Ways of God, she was able to reevaluate her obedience to the Agooji Way of life. Her interest and commitment to the Agooji Way of life was waning.

A merchant of death, like Chinwe, knew that her life was expendable and would readily be forfeited by her diminishing attention to detail. The ventures of excitement and misery she enacted had to come to an end. The journey she traveled to redirect her life was neither a fairy tale nor an easy task, but it was directed by God. Chinwe had an "Awakening" to her Purpose. The how and the ways Chinwe was able to extricate herself from her association with the Kingdom of Dahomey, King Agaja, and the "Agooji Way of Life" is a complete story in itself. One that could only be orchestrated by God.

Bruised, scarred, and humbled, Chinwe found herself back home among her people, the Bubis.

Chinwe and Rufaro fell in love and began to settle into a loving relationship. Their union produced two girls, Rehema and Mudiwa. Chinwe saw the same fire and fearlessness that consumed her at their age. She was going to make sure that her daughters were prepared for life, both physically and spiritually. She also guided them in the skills needed to hunt deep in the bush. Rehema and Mudiwa became skilled with the club, the knife, and the bow. Chinwe still possessed her "Ndevu ya Muda Mrefu," the art and flow of using it, which gave her girls an unfair advantage in stick fighting games.

Rufaro had no problems with Chinwe preparing his daughters for life and war. All this preparation was tempered with a love for God and obedience to His Directives for their lives. Rufaro's life had been based in the Bubi Military; he had served as the head of the Tree Leopards for Chief Zuberi. Rufaro had had a similar "Awakening" to Chinwe's Awakening and had rededicated himself to God and his family. While he established the direction for his family, he also wanted them prepared for any circumstance that might occur in their lives. His girls were not tame, docile creatures looking for a man to dominate and meet needs that were out of their grasp. Rufaro's daughters had been taught by Chinwe to "endure and achieve." His girls were seeking partners looking for completion, not servitude. They were looking for a man who could appreciate having a woman that could complete them in any endeavor. A man who depended on God and could love them in their worst moments. A man who could make them swoon, feel beautiful and loved in his arms. A man they could call Husband! Masego had met those qualifications for Rufaro and Chinwe, but he excelled in those attributes by Rehema's standards. So she became Masego's wife.

The wedding ceremony for Rehema and Masego was a week-long festive event full of pageantry and panache. There were guest from neighboring clans, the Kombe (Come-bay), Yoruba (Yoh-rue-baw), Fang, Lengi (Lenghee), and Mabea (Ah-bay-ah) to name a few. Colorful and festive in their ethnic attire, the wedding guests were treated to the best the Beti-Pahuin and Bubi people could offer. Chiefs Zuberi and Chibueze assured a good time was had by all. All were thankful for the blessings God was bestowing on this young couple. The concluding celebrations saw the participants make spiritual offerings of thanks and gratitude to the Most High.

As the wedding guests returned to their homes, Masego and Rehema settled into a life of completeness. They appeared to do everything together; Masego and

Rehema even hunted together miles away from their village. They would go deep into the bush for days and would return with meat for themselves and their village. Their neighbors were so appreciative that they made certain the young couple had plenty of ground grains and vegetables. This allowed Rehema and Masego more time to hunt and bond in the solitude of the bush. This togetherness in their own little world was producing a tie that would strengthen their completeness as one.

Masego spent very little time at the gathering spot for the men of the village. He would appear occasionally to be politically correct and sociable, but he had no great interest in gossiping and sharing tales of exploits. Exploits and rumors that grew in greater importance with every telling combined with sometime malicious gossip was not Masego's idea of fun. Rehema was able to avoid a great deal of the cackling done by the women while washing clothes and grinding grains. She, too, would attend sporadically in order to be politically correct and sociable. Her delight was being in the company of her husband.

The people in the village would chuckle at their devotion to each other and gave them the name Mapacha ya Upendo, the Love Twins. Rehema and Masego were delighted with their title of "Love Twins" around the village. They didn't think they were doing anything special, just what was in their hearts. Masego and Rehema were content; now they were just waiting on God to bless them with their family and continue their legacy in the Beti-Pahuin Clan.

Rehema was glowing with the thought that their first child was coming soon; they were praising God that this may be the beginning of their legacy. The ultimate goal of a couple who understands being complete in obedience to God.

Their legacy became a reality with the birth of their daughter Chipo (She-po). Rehema and Masego were so full with joy that, in their minds, they realigned the sun to rise and set on Chipo. Masego and Rehema's future dreams were now a complete reality that only needed effort and work.

Little did Rehema and Masego understand or realize that a "Clash of Dreams" a world away would alter their existence and dictate their future. A future of tribulations and trials that only their faith in God could intercede and bring them through. Enduring would become their way of life to achieve their goals.

In her blissful moments with Masego, Rehema could not have foretold how the experiences and training she received from her mother Chinwe would allow her to forge the glue that would build her family for generations to come.

3

THE CLASH OF DREAMS
(THOUGH THE HEAVENS MAY FALL!)

John Stewart was an Englishman whose business would take him to Boston and Virginia. Stewart was a Sinecure. Sinecures lived in England and delegated the collection of customs to agents living in the colonies. Being a Sinecure was very profitable for him. John Stewart soon found out quickly that being in the colonies would fulfill his dreams.

The collection of customs was the biggest racket and most lucrative business, next to the slave trade, in the British Empire. Stewart was accepting huge bribes from colonial shippers who were smuggling into the thirteen colonies molasses, sugar, tea, and fruits from Dutch and French colonies. It was completely against the law for the English colonies to trade with foreign countries and their colonies, but a good price was a good price. When they needed lead or glass or spices, their concern was cost, and John Stewart and his fellow Sinecures and Custom Agents were there to meet the colonists' needs and their own personal greed.

The major component of Mercantilism, which ruled the British Empire at that time, was that the colonies existed to enrich the mother country, in this case, England. John Stewart firmly believed that true Englishmen should be the recipients of all the benefits that Mercantilism presented. To this end, it became necessary to send his cousin Joshua Bellington to Virginia as a Custom Agent. Virginia had the biggest cash crop in the Thirteen Colonies, tobacco, plus it cultivated the dreams of Stewart. John Stewart would situate himself in Boston, where the true opportunities of wealth were embedded through illegal activities in sea commerce.

Stewart did not like the cold of Boston, but Boston was the leading seaport in the colonies and his personal "cash cow." The opportunity was too great for a man consumed with his vision of happiness to resist. He must press on if he was to become "the man of leisure" that he felt John Stewart's birthright and legacy demanded.

His plan was simple, he would continue to skim and cheat in Boston; he justified his actions based on his belief "that everybody was doing it." Joshua would work as a Custom Agent in Virginia where his real mission was to scout out a suitable piece of property that Stewart could purchase. Stewart wanted at least ten thousand acres to start his estate called "Haven on the Pond Plantation." Haven on the Pond would be his sanctuary and eventually his home. Having identified twelve thousand acres in Virginia's rolling hills and purchasing it, Haven on the Pond Plantation came into existence. Bellington was given the task of functioning as the acting owner of Haven on the Pond in Stewart's absence.

Joshua Bellington had learned his trade well; Joshua became the Custom Agent extraordinaire. Bellington could circumvent any law related to trade and commerce. Joshua was really able to increase their coffers when the British government enacted the Navigation Acts, which the colonists called the Salutary Neglect. This was the provision that basically said that the cost of collecting taxes outweighed the taxes themselves. Bellington knew his commodities well. Because he was in the warmer climate of Virginia, the colonists' needs were shaped differently than the colonists in Boston. His proximity to the Spanish, Dutch, and French West Indies allowed him to construct deals with Spanish colonists in Florida and French colonists in the Bayous of Louisiana. He had purchased boats that allowed him to introduce seafood delicacies from the Chesapeake Bay to the palate of the aristocrats of Virginia and others. Bellington's fleet of boats and schooners also assisted in rum-running with his cousin John Stewart in Boston. He had become very proficient in every aspect of tobacco from growing, to curing, to selling, to exporting, but there was one commodity that he became the leading expert on, Slaves.

Joshua had no personal animosity against those "Darkies"; it was just good business. He recognized that the slaves were coming from different backgrounds and skill sets, and if he could identify their complete worth, their value would increase four-fold. John Stewart was pleased with Joshua's advancements in Virginia. When functioning in Boston, he kept his opinions on slavery to himself, but when in Virginia, his opinion was "Darkies serve a purpose to achieving my goals."

Joshua Bellington had gone into business with several merchants and opened their own slave stores in Virginia and the Carolinas. He specialized in selling field hands in bundles, house servants, and sex slaves. Joshua had no problem expending additional time and money in preparing those "darkies" that he felt would become good house servants and great sex slaves.

Bellington would also purchase slaves who had been the offspring of white plantation owners. He found that even though it was against the law to teach slaves to read and write, some slave owners would do such with their offspring from a slave woman. These slaves were of the highest value, not only on the underground slave market, but for the operation of Haven on the Pond Plantation.

One such slave was James. James had been born a slave, the son of Thaddeus Olgebroom, owner of Lost Oak Plantation and his slave Sally. James knew nothing of his heritage, but his mother told him about her grandfather, who was a great chieftain with too many cattle and goats to count. Sally would share stories of her grandfather's village and their people. Sally couldn't remember great details because she had been born in the colonies as a slave and tried to recall the oral history told to her, and now she was sharing it to her son. She did remember the name of her grandfather, Kamau. James's spirit was strengthened with the knowledge of his ancestor's name, "Kamau," and a word Sally taught him in their native dialect, "Ubuntu," "I am Because We Are." This gave James great comfort in knowing he was part of a "Legacy" and that one day his dream of "Freedom" could become a reality. His mother Sally had time to share with her son because her duties on Olgebroom's Plantation were quite direct, wash dishes after meals in the big house and be Thaddeus Olgebroom's sex toy on demand. Her quarters were next to the kitchen for his convenience.

James was a bright young man who possessed a very logical approach to accomplishing goals, plus his skill with numbers was remarkable. His approach to business was increasing Haven on the Pond's income threefold. James's proclivity to detail was creating solutions to problems before John Stewart or Joshua Bellington realized they were concerns. A very erudite and serious young man, James knew he was treated differently from other house slaves and field slaves, but he saw no difference between them and himself. James believed a life of dictated servitude was not how one human being should treat another human being. James would use his limited power of influence to lessen his fellow slaves' suffering or create an upsurge in Haven on the Pond's slaves' wellbeing at every opportunity. He never forgot "I am Because We Are," Ubuntu. Joshua Bellington was proud of James's efforts at Haven on the Pond, and John Stewart wished he had a son of white heritage that possessed James's brilliance, dedication, and commitment.

As political direction began to ebb and flow in directions not favorable for either John Stewart or Haven on the Pond, it was becoming increasingly clear that he would have to return to England; the loss of revenue he was experiencing was becoming too great. The Townshend Acts had been passed in Britain and were beginning to wreak total havoc with his operations in the colonies;

taxes were being imposed and enforced on Stewart's most lucrative smuggling items.

He had been childhood friends with Charles Townshend, who was now the Chancellor of the Exchequer and the author of the Townshend Acts. Stewart was hoping to meet with Townshend and plead the need to rescind or reduce the impact of these Acts. Townshend took this action because the British Coffers were losing too much potential revenue. Seven hundred thousand pounds (British Pounds) of goods were coming into the colonies legally and only two thousand pounds were being received in taxes. A disparaging situation that could not continue if the British Empire was to survive. The four Townshend Acts, approved between June 15th and July 2nd of 1767, would crack down on the skimming of funds in the colonies. If these crackdowns by the British government continued, John Stewart would find his dream of a "life of leisure" destroyed. He knew that intervention on his part was critical and would require his return to England.

Stewart had decided to bring James along with him on his return to England. James would be a very valuable asset in the work he needed to accomplish in England, plus he wanted to show that slaves served a valuable position in British Society and that he personally was saving them from their heathen nature.

John Stewart and James departed from Virginia for the long sea voyage to England. While departing from the pier, James got his first look and smells of a slave ship unloading its human cargo. James was expecting to enjoy the solitude of the sea over the next six to eight weeks. Stewart had been a member of the Scottish Episcopal Church since birth and had acquainted James with the tradition and services of the Episcopal Church in their Virginia community. James would now have the opportunity to read and study the Bible that his master had given him, without having to be discreet.

James found the Bible intriguing and confusing at the same time on the long voyage. The most intriguing part was that the Bible expanded on and completed all of the spiritual teachings that his mother had taught him and the attributes she wanted him to present to the world as her son. The confusing part was, since it provided an understanding and pathway for life and so many people seemed committed to it, why did their conduct, actions, and treatment of other children of God attest to an opposite belief and use of the Bible? To James, this dichotomy was a very dangerous posture to take in the presence of God.

He hoped one day to discover the solution to this dilemma of life. Unfortunately, right now he was on a ship heading to England to help conduct scurrilous business for an amoral man. Just maybe when they attended services at St. Paul's Cathedral in England, he would be able to obtain a better understanding and a remedy to this quandary.

John Stewart's plans were to conduct all necessary political and personal business in the time he planned to stay in England. He had calculated that this would be his last lengthy visit before permanently moving to Virginia to implement his plans for a "life of leisure." His meeting with Chancellor Townshend was calamitous. Stewart insinuated that Townshend was trying to destroy the Crown by strangling commerce in the colonies, and Townshend accused Stewart of high crimes and misdemeanors. Townshend promised John Stewart the gallows once the appropriate evidence came to light. Their childhood friendship and spats had turned into a much more severe adult predicament. As the situation appeared to have no interest in deescalating, James felt the need to interject some calmness and diplomatic direction to reduce the tension. Having achieved his goal of de-escalation in that contentious Townshend-Stewart meeting, James continued with Stewart about the English countryside putting Stewart's business in order.

England was an interesting place. He enjoyed attending church services and Bible studies and enjoyed the fact that he didn't have to hide the fact that he could read and write. He met some wonderful people in the church and began to develop a spiritual and personal bond with them.

British customs and sayings were a little more difficult to grasp for James. The British had a saying: "English Air is too pure to be breathed by a slave"; when he first heard this, it scared him. His thought was that since he was a slave, these English people were going to kill him. Fortunately with the help of his church friends, especially Granville Sharp, he learned that it meant that no person should be a slave in England and that it dated back to Queen Elizabeth the First. The question that began to weigh heavy in his mind was "If I am in England, then why am I still a slave?" James was in a state of mental flux, but he had business to attend to with the master John Stewart. Their next stop would be an important business meeting in an area where he had very little familiarity, maritime insurance.

Stewart had bought part ownership in a fleet of slave ships. His scheme was to load the ship with slaves and an overweight cargo of smuggled cocoa. Cocoa was worth its weight in gold in the colonies and England. The British government kept extremely tight regulations on the import and export of cocoa, making it as expensive as the most exotic spices from the colony of India. Stewart knew that the ships ran a dangerous risk of sinking and could not make the oceanic voyage to the colonies over laden. Stewart knew that the average loss of merchandize, slaves, on a voyage was about twenty percent. His crews were instructed to load their ships with between fourteen and eighteen percent of undesirable slaves, lame, old, impaired but not sick. In the early stage of the voyage, the crew would throw those less desirous slaves into the ocean to drown, lessening the load on the ship. Strict instructions were given to not waste provisions on this group of undesirable slaves.

John Stewart along with James were now on their way to Stewart's old hangout, Lloyd's Coffee House, the precursor to Lloyd's of London, in order to secure the insurance he would need to make his scheme extremely lucrative. At Lloyd's Coffee House he could secure the slave insurance needed to cover his loss of merchandize at sea. The insurance would provide him with the necessary revenue for the undesirable slaves they disposed of at sea and make for a safer trip with his smuggled cocoa.

James felt his master's conduct and schemes becoming totally intolerable. He had never been exposed to the inner workings of the slave trade; to him, it was just vicious and cruel. His personal inner torment was beginning to overwhelm him.

The state of flux that James was experiencing was reaching a boiling point. For the first time in his life he started thinking about being free. Freedom was a foreign concept to a man who had known nothing but servitude and disrespect. Now, the concept of freedom was creeping into his conscience and was beginning to flood his soul. He began to share more and more of his angst concerning his current situation. Expounding on the life of servitude he was expected to render until he drew his last breath with his church friends.

James's only solace was in enjoying the peace he obtained while sitting in a church pew and meditating. He had also started his own little library of books. He was currently enjoying the *Canterbury Tales* by Geoffrey Chaucer and was looking forward to reading Milton's *Paradise Lost* and Dante Alighieri's *Divine Comedy*. James found immense pleasure in escaping reality by becoming a participant in the book he was reading. He fantasized about having a room filled from ceiling to floor with books; it would be his private sanctuary. A place of solitude and freedom, but then the cold reality of his plight and his future of servitude would ebb in and destroy his dream. James, the man-slave with no last name, was determined to have his dream of freedom and to have it now!

James's direction of action gained the clarity that it needed once he resolved one major inner issue. He knew that in England their belief was if you were a Christian then you could not be considered a slave. James was aware of several Africans in London who were considered free because they had become baptized. His dilemma of conscience was that he believed too strongly in his relationship with God to play with his eternal soul. He would not use baptism as a ploy for his own self gain.

His friends at church had been urging him to be baptized because they could see a special gifting of God upon him, and they were true abolitionists. James enjoyed arriving early to Bible study so he could sit in a pew and meditate. On this occasion, an older man was in deep prayer at the altar. When he finished praying, he noticed James and went directly toward him. Now James had seen this man in church on several occasions, but they had never shared more than a nod and a quick hello or goodbye. The older gentleman ventured to the pew were James was sitting, he smiled and looked James in the eye and said: "God has work for you to do." He smiled at James and excused himself and left.

Complete clarity and a sense of total peace engulfed James. He knew what he had to do and began to address his issues step by step.

James's first step was to become baptized. His friends at church were so elated that they began to bicker over who would be his godparent. Finally, the issue was re solved; James would have three godparents, John Marlow, Thomas Walkin, and Elizabeth Cade. His baptism was a splendid affair that was very private. Everyone knew that John Stewart would be very displeased with James becoming a Christian and would attempt to stop it. James's second step was to take a last name; this would bring completeness to his earthly manhood. He choose Somerset, so James the slave became James Somerset. His third step was to escape from John Stewart.

James Somerset planned his escape very carefully, with the help of his three godparents, Elizabeth Cade, John Marlow, and Thomas Walkin. The plan was thorough and complete that the four of them enacted in November. James Somerset was a free man, but what they had not counted on was the ferocity of John Stewart's response.

John Stewart, on realizing that James had escaped, was furious. He first hired two slave catchers and immediately put them on James's trail and shared his tendencies. He then contacted his old friend Captain John Knowles, skipper of the slave ship *Ann and Mary*. Stewart then made arrangements to sell James to Captain Knowles who would sell the slave James to a sugarcane plantation in Jamaica, where he was sure to be worked to death within five years. Stewart would muse: "How ungrateful was this darkie heathen, after all I had done for him." Stewart's last words on the matter of James was: "I'll teach him!"

James Somerset's freedom was short lived; it only lasted a month. He was captured by the slave catchers, beaten, and taken to Captain Knowles. Knowles bound, whipped, and placed James on the ship *Ann and Mary*. The ship that was awaiting the voyage to Jamaica, ready to offer James nothing but certain despair and death on a sugarcane plantation. Not to be outdone or to give up, Somerset's godparents consulted with a dear friend and abolitionist, Granville Sharp, who was a prominent member of English society. Under Sharp's guidance, Thomas Walkin, Elizabeth Cade, and John Marlow petitioned the Court of the King's Bench for a "Writ of Habeas Corpus" on behalf of James Somerset. A "Writ of Habeas Corpus" required that the detainee, in this case James Somerset, must be brought in person before the court. Captain Knowles had to release James Somerset and present him before the court.

William Murray, First Earl of Mansfield, Lord Chief Justice of the King's Court, released Somerset to his own recognizance until his trial in January. James's godparents, with Granville Sharp's assistance, had put together an illustrious group of five lawyers, including the noted Irish attorney and orator John Philpot Curran. The argument before the court was Colonial Law vs British Law.

The court proceedings took longer than normal, with both sides battling points and counterpoints and long declamations about individual rights. Lord Mansfield knew that this was a potential "Gordian Knot," or worse a "Sword of Damocles," that would hang over the entire

British Empire. Realizing the significance of his ruling William Murray, First Earl of Mansfield, Lord Chief Justice of the King's Court, took his time in rendering a decision. He knew that his decision could galvanize the colonies in America into a unified opposition against the Crown. Slavery was the key to the southern colonies success. Any ruling against or that created a hindrance to slavery could have a domino effect and major impact on southern economic growth. The northern colonies who were already in protest over taxes; the crackdown on smuggling and proper representation in legislative matters would welcome the support of the southern colonies. Their thinking was they could confront the issue of slavery at another time and another place.

Lord Mansfield was well aware of the potential powder keg to the British Empire he could be creating by cementing a united front within the thirteen colonies in America. He also knew his moral responsibility as the Lord Chief Justice of the King's Court and as a "Man of God," who was raising two grandnieces, Dido Elizabeth Bell (born 1761), who was born a slave, and her cousin Elizabeth Murray (born 1760), who was white. One White and One Black but he loved them both dearly.

William Murray, First Earl of Mansfield, Lord Chief Justice of the King's Court, rendered his decision on June 22, 1772. Lord Mansfield ruled that neither the Common Law of England nor legislative actions of Parliament supported slavery. Therefore any slave entering or leaving England would be granted their freedom. This became known as the Mansfield Decree. ***"Fiat justitia ruat caelum" – "Let justice be done though the heavens fall."***

James Somerset had been given his freedom! He and his supporters both Black and White praised God and celebrated his freedom and what it meant to nearly fifteen thousand Africans living in England. Mansfield did not address the issue of slavery in the British Empire, that would have to be dealt with later, but he provided a breath of fresh air for those residing in England proper.

James Somerset went on to have a "Life of Service" instead of a "Life of Servitude." He worked in the church and eventually taught the Bible study class he attended. James married and had three children who never had to be caught in slavery and could cultivate their dreams in "Freedom." He also worked with Granville Sharp on the Society for Effecting the Abolition of the Slave Trade. Somerset worked closely with the Black Poor in the London area, feeding them both spiritually and naturally. James Somerset became close friends with Olaudah Equiano and Charles Ignatius Sancho, both prominent Blacks in England. He also provided some opposition to the Committee for the Relief of Black Poor's idea of returning Blacks to Africa.

Unbeknownst to James Somerset, his devotion to God and willingness to persevere would impact an African couple thousands of miles away named Masego and Rehema and, eventually, the colonies in America themselves.

4

ANEW!

It was a fierce attack. Chief Apunda and the Clear People had elevated the skill of kidnapping to an art form. Their attack on the Beti-Pahuin Clan was complete and devastating to the lives of Masego, Rehema, Chipo, and their fellow villagers. They had been taken but not together; Rehema and Masego did not know if the other had escaped the attack, was taken in the attack, or died in the onslaught. Their world had been decimated and thrown into great turmoil.

Five weeks earlier Rehema had given birth to a baby girl that they named Chipo. The young couple were excited because their child made their family complete and ensured them a legacy! They had great plans for Chipo and were already speculating about her future, but the attack by Apunda and the Clear People was rearranging the concept of family for Masego and Rehema. Masego had been taken while delivering meat from his hunt to an elderly couple in the Clan. Rehema and Chipo were seized while gathering water at the river.

Masego was shackled and brought to the location where the men were being yoked together on poles. Rehema, having Chipo stripped from her arms, was shackled and moved to a cattle pen. Chipo, upon being taken from her mother, was immediately thrown into a "guinea-sack." The Clear People liked placing the infants in "guinea-sacks" because it reduced the resistance, plus during the march to the sea, it kept the captive parents focused on their infants' wellbeing since they had no way of knowing whose infant was still alive. All they could do was pray, because escaping and leaving their families was not an option.

The march to the departure area near the sea was slow and arduous. Brutality, death, sickness, hunger, and disease became their constant companions on this trail of tears. For the women and young girls, it was a much more hideous and sinister venture. They were raped, abused, and sodomized and forced into unnatural sex acts at the whims of the Clear People. The Beti-Pahuins had never seen such brutality, viciousness, and hate from another human being in their tribal history.

Rehema and Masego would not see each other until they reached the holding cells, a day's journey from the sea. Their encounter was brief from afar, but it was good to know that their spiritual and physical mate was still alive. Though they were separated, they were still complete. Their focus was now centered on their child, Chipo. Did she survive the march to the sea? Was she alright? Which sack is she in? How am I going to rescue her? God help me!

Their individual concern for Chipo outweighed anything they had suffered or would suffer. It was this concern for their family that caused them to endure when enduring did not seem like a reasonable option. Their separate but unifying prayer was: ***"God, give me the strength to endure; until you bring this madness to an end."***

Masego knew that in order to develop a plan of deliverance for his family, he first had to begin to understand more about the Clear People's habits and language. Their language was nothing he had heard before, but he could begin to absorb it by gathering the meaning of small things first. While all those around him were angry and talking about escape and killing the Clear People, Masego was studying their communication through motion and inflection. Their language and their habits were becoming clearer to him. To Masego, these were going to become the necessary components to bringing this incursion of abuse, suffering, and pain to an end. Every breath he took made it more evident that time was on his side.

He learned several important factors as his proficiency in understanding their language and ways grew. First was their favorite term for Masego and all the African captives, no matter what Clan they were from, was "darkies." Second, that the Clear People's Clan was called the English. Third, they were being held longer than usual because the great sea was mad with wind-driven waves and storms they called hurricanes, information Masego had gathered by listening to their stories of peril. He also discovered that these winds, waves, and storms occurred every year at the same time, and it was very dangerous for boats to be on the great sea at that time. Fourth, it would be several more weeks before it would be safe enough to travel on the great sea that they called ocean. Fifth, there were two boats waiting to take the captives to a place called the "New World"; the name of the boats were the *Zong* and the *Phoenix*.

The next revelation could not be measured and stored as pertinent information necessary to enact his plans for family reunification. This tidbit of information was acquired from spending hours of learning their language and habits and was sending Masego into a full rage.

Focus and deliberate planning had escaped him, and all he wanted to do was kill these people with no regard to his wellbeing or that of his family. As the guards were sitting around and consuming large portions of an intoxicating beverage, they began talking about what they had done and were going to do to Rehema and the other female captives. This was too much for Masego to handle. His pride and honor had been completely destroyed by his feeling of guilt for not being able to defend his wife. He felt the pain and anguish Rehema must had been enduring and felt that he was less than a man for not giving all he had to give, to his death, to protect her. Life and planning together a future no longer had any meaning to him. Masego wanted to kill all these evil human beings, maim those he could not kill, or annihilate anything associated with Clear People and their way of life. He cried to God: "WHY? WHY? WHY? WHAT AM I SUPPOSED TO DO? THIS IS NOT WORTH LIVING!" Revenge and hatred took control over his emotions and thinking and lulled him to sleep amongst the squalor he had been placed in.

When he awoke he swore that the sun would not set before he punished these Clear People, today! There had been many riots by some of his fellow captives and even some had committed suicide to avoid being subjected to what Masego was enduring. Now he did not care about any kind of a future and was ready to join their ranks to accomplish his revenge.

Every third day they were taken to an area where they were able to wash away the filth of the holding pens. The Clear People did this to reduce disease and sickness to their valuable merchandise of captive "darkies." This is when and where Masego would put his plan into action. All he needed was his hands to be free. He was a very skilled warrior and hunter, but his skills had been heightened by association with his in-laws. His mother-in-law Chinwe had been a "Reaper" in the Agooji Army and an expert in afflicting swift death on an enemy. His father-in-law Rufaro, having been the captain of the Tree Leopards for Chief Zuberi, had instilled stealth and effectiveness in Masego's ability to attack and destroy. While Chinwe and Rufaro shared liberally with Masego about the skills they had developed decades ago, it was Rehema who made them real in his life. She taught Masego what he didn't know about the art of surviving and killing. She instilled the training her mother had imparted in her into him. They could be summed up in two words *"Endure and Achieve."*

Masego's plan was simple: while his hands were free, he would place himself close to the gate of the washing pen; this would place him next to a guard. When washing time was over he would kill that guard using the cross that hung around his neck. Masego believed that the cross that every Clear Person wore around their neck must be the unifying symbol of this evil clan of people. He would take the guard's knife. Masego did not know how the thunder stick that they called a gun worked. What he did know was the gun only thundered once and then took a long time to thunder again. He knew the knife would allow him to do more damage in a shorter amount of time. He would incite a riot, and they would rush out of the wash pen and kill the Clear People.

Masego, the diplomat, the warrior, the husband, the father, had no end plan to his strategy. He wasn't looking to escape. He wasn't trying to save Rehema and Chipo. He was engulfed in hatred and rage. This was totally unlike his normal nature, but he didn't care. He was prepared to die, and he was going to take as many Clear People as possible with him.

As they took the iron halo from around his neck and freed his hands, Masego overheard the guards talking about the African infants who had been taken. It seems that several of the infants came down with dysentery; of the fifty or so infants, thirty-five had died in their holding pen awaiting the storms to subside. The owner of the holding pens decided that maintaining the remaining infants was too costly. As far as he was concerned, infants were no longer a profitable proposition, so they were murdered and then incinerated.

Chipo was dead! His baby girl of delight, his legacy, their fountain of joy, their reason to exist, Rehema and Masego's creation and gift from God was gone!

The firestorm of hate and revenge that had reached catastrophic levels was subsiding instead of increasing as he thought it should. It was being tempered by something that he could not understand nor did he want to accept it. The news of his daughter's demise was acting as a backfire to a dangerous brushfire. Masego had expected this tragic news to magnify his rage, but he was gaining purpose and direction from God. It was no longer about him but about his love for Rehema. He must survive for her!

No one would die today; he had too much to do to survive for his wife and the memory of their baby Chipo.

The first thing Masego had to do was to get back into relationship with his God in order to dissipate the hatred and rage that had blinded his vision and purpose. His vision and purpose was to get back his family and survive until God brought this madness to an end. He was going to endure and achieve!

Having regained his peace and balance in the midst of this life changing storm, he endured. Now it was time to achieve his goal of gaining his and Rehema's freedom.

Conversation among the Clear People was becoming more contentious. Things were not going according to their plans and anticipations. They had not been paid, and the storms in the great sea were destroying many boats. The Clear People were losing too much money with the delays. Something was going to have to be done. Fifteen hundred (1,500) darkies were in need of transportation to the New World. Captain William Gregson of the *Zong* and Captain Robert Stubbs of the *Phoenix* decided that they would brave whatever storms that were in the great sea. The situation they were confronting could not be maintained much longer if they were to achieve their expectations of profit.

They had decided to do the "tight packing" method of the "darkies." Captain Stubbs would pack seven hundred (700) darkies on his ship, the *Phoenix*, and head for Jamaica in the West Indies. Captain Gregson would "tight pack" eight hundred (800) darkies on the *Zong* and would head for Charleston in the colonies. Stubbs was to pack his ship first and would leave four days before Gregson and the *Zong* departed.

It would be a short march to the edge of the sea. Masego's prayer was that he would be blessed to glimpse his wife Rehema, just to know that she was alive, and continued his prayer with the hope they would be placed on the same boat. The path of the march to the sea brought them down through winding terrains and swampy areas with pockets of quicksand. A short journey, but a dangerous one. Their progress was delayed by death and injuries, turning a one-day trip into a three-day journey. All during this trek, their African handlers taunted them about the "Beach of Sorrow" and the "Door of No Return." Those handlers taunted the captives about the "Beach of Sorrow" and the "Door of No Return" as being the places where they would finally get what they had long deserved as "Haifai," "Undesirables."

The "Beach of Sorrow" was where they would be prepared for what these African handlers called the "Njia ya Kati," the Middle Passage. The handlers smirked and heckled Masego and the other captives about the Middle Passage and their ability to endure it. They told the captives that the Middle Passage would be a "hali ya akili," a state of mind. These African handlers, supported by the Clear People, would enjoy the thought of administering their hate in additional doses of pain and punishment on the "Beach of Sorrow,"

On the "Beach of Sorrow" the captives would now be housed and shackled in little dark huts on wooden planks for bedding; they were six feet long, three feet wide with three feet of height between each bedding. They were stacked six beddings high; this was to simulate what their housing would be like aboard ship. They were forced to be shackled to this bedding twenty-three hours a day. Their availability to drinking water was going to be extremely restricted on the "Beach of Sorrow" to simulate their rationing aboard ship. Not only was it restricted, but it contained rotten citrus cut up in it; this was an attempt to delay the on-set of scurvy abroad the ship. The Beach of Sorrow was white sand, spotted with patches of blood from beatings, abuses, and branding of the captives for the next two weeks. Another trial for them to endure.

As Masego entered the "Beach of Sorrow," he saw an enclave of women captives eating. Wherever they were taking Masego and the men, they would have to pass within fifty feet of these women. As he grew closer to them, a familiar smile greeted him from afar. It was Rehema; she had survived the final march to the sea! It was not wise for families to make it known that their relative was in the same vicinity; this would guarantee that they would not be placed on the same ship and would only increase their torment on the "Beach of Sorrow."

Rehema's eyes glittered and danced as she gave a smile to Masego; he spontaneously reciprocated in kind, and for a moment, they were blissful once again knowing that they had endured. For a mega moment, time stood still, then Rehema's look turned to one of sorrow and despair. Masego knew where her thoughts had spun to, the welfare of their child Chipo. Masego masterfully gave her an expression of reassurance that Chipo was fine and thriving. He would carry the weight of the loss of their child by himself until he and Rehema were joined together again.

The "Beach of Sorrow" produced all that the handlers had promised and then some. They were now going to be introduced to the "Door of No Return." Chained to walls, they peered out "The Door of No Return" that provided the only ventilation they had. It opened to the great sea. There was nothing but water, more water than any of the African captives had ever seen. A view of hopelessness that tempered their optimism and destroyed their psyche. Producing a realization that everything familiar to their existence was soon to be snatched from them spiritually, emotionally, and physically. They were chained to the walls of the long hallway to the "Door of No Return," a vision of endless nothingness. The only way Masego knew how to persist and endure through this spiritual, emotional, and physical attack was to pray to God, and pray he did.

The male captives were loaded on to the *Phoenix* first. Here was where resistance was the greatest, but given the captives' weaken condition, the bursts of resistance were very short and ineffective. Masego's bedding plank was at the top of a stacking this provided him a view through the stairway to the top deck of the *Phoenix*. As he lay there, he watched as the women captives boarded the ship. There she was his bride, his beauty, his reason to endure and achieve his primary goal of reunification, his completeness, Rehema.

She was battered and abused emotionally, physically, and sexually, but he knew her spirit. He knew that Rehema would die before she allowed anything or anyone to interfere with her relationship with God. Masego now spent his time with God, meditating on how he was going to help Rehema with her healing process once this nightmare was over.

{Author's Privilege—Man's inhumanity to Man has neither limits nor boundaries. An array of atrocities have occurred and continue to occur. The Middle Passage, the Holocaust, the Cambodian Massacre, the Armenian Genocide, the American Indians' Trail of Tears, the Nanking Massacre, and the hordes of African Massacres and genocide have led to countless attempts of genocide today. Make yourself aware by visiting www.genocidewatch.com}

The ocean was rough, creating sicknesses that the captives had never experienced. Masego never thought a boat could tip and swirl as much as the *Phoenix* was doing two weeks into the voyage and not sink. His experience at sea was adding additional misery that he did not anticipate. His concern, however, turned to Rehema. He was concerned about her welfare and how she was enduring the abuse she was being forced to accept. His prayers completely centered around God giving the love of his life the strength she needed to endure. Masego's only source of relief only occurred through peaceful meditation with God. He would be lost in thoughts of how Rehema and he would work on healing together from this catastrophic infringement on their lives. Masego was prepared, once God ended this madness, to begin building their future in order to achieve what God has for them.

The storms would not cease. The wind had never felt this piercing at home nor did it carry such a weapon as hail. Ice and cold were impacting the captives in ways they had never experienced. Something was happening that Masego didn't understand. The sun was no longer rising in front of the boat and setting behind it. It was now rising on the left side of the boat and setting on the right side.

Masego did not know what this change in direction meant. Whether it was a scheduled turn of direction or one caused by the volatility of the storm, all he knew was that Rehema and he were going to be thrust into a hostile environment based on his experience with these Clear People. It didn't matter to him because, when God decided to bring this madness to an end, they would survive. Even though Rehema and Masego were endur-ing the degradation, abuse, murder of family and friends, and, particularly, the death of Chipo, they would achieve, no matter what.

The storm was a blessing to Rehema. While the tu-multuous sea had the same effect on her as it did the other captives, it diminished the ship's crew opportunities to sexually abuse her and the other female captives. The height of the storm was her most peaceful. All crew members were required to be at their duty stations constantly. It made it impossible for them to make incursions into the African females' area. Rehema was left with an opportunity to meditate with the Creator and strengthen her resolve to endure for her family, Masego, and Chipo.

The Creator would provide her the resolve she needed. God would remind her, ***"I will restore you; hold on to Me in the midst of your pain; I hurt with you; they are misusing their free will; your future is bright..."*** Rehema believed God and would not allow her current situation to dictate her attitude. She took every opportunity while being abused to pray for her husband and daughter. She did not know if Masego and Chipo were on the same boat, but she knew they would be together again. Rehema also noticed the change of directions but had no idea of the significance of it.

The sea began to surrender its anger, and it appeared that Captain Stubbs had regained control of his ship. The *Phoenix* was battered but still seaworthy. Captain Stubbs' concern was the issue of provisions and the fact that the storm had placed his ship in a position closer to England and much farther away from Jamaica. His options were limited, and his decision was clear; he must land in England. It was an option he did not want to exercise, but if he didn't, it would put himself and his crew in jeopardy. Captain Stubbs had no concern for his cargo; those darkies were insured, so the revenue from them would not be lost.

That damn Mansfield Decree; since it had been enacted, slavers like Captain Robert Stubbs had lost thousands of darkies not to storms but to a law. They were too close to the coast of England to drown those darkies; bodies would wash up on the shore and negate his insurance claim, and one load of darkies was not worth intentionally sinking his ship. There was nowhere else for him to go. England it would be; he would chalk this loss up to providence.

5

MTU–BURE (FREE — MAN)

The *Phoenix* would dock at the first available port in England. Captain Stubbs was looking to make land at Hastings; he thought a deal, or a bribe, could be formulated there. Hastings was a little out of the way but never did receive a great deal of slave traffic. Now with the Mansfield Decree in full implementation, English ports were destinations of last resort. Stubbs had no options available to him but English ports.

Mr. Victor Farthingham was a man of considerable height and great girth, and he was the dock master, in charge of all day-to-day activities occurring in Hastings. He had been appointed by the Vice Admiral of the Coast for Sussex County John Ashburnham. Lord Ashburnham was a stickler for details and documentation. Victor Farthingham was Lord Ashburnham's type of man; they both had been involved in England's Seven Years War. They and the major of the marine garrison, Cordell

Smith, participated in the "ships of the line" that had attacked Morro Castile and captured Havana in 1762. The three of them worked well in controlling and maintaining shipping and trading in Sussex County.

Mr. Farthingham had a great disdain for slavers; to him, slavers were the lowest form of human life known to mankind. Victor Farthingham had another reason for his great contempt for slavers; it was the most precious thing in his life, his granddaughter Victoria. Victoria was a mulatto, born to his daughter Esther Farthingham-Sancho and her husband Charles Ignatius Sancho. Charles Ignatius Sancho was recognized in Great Britain as a composer, a writer, and an actor. His fame was well acknowledged throughout the British Isles as a "fine Negro." He and Esther were extremely active in the British anti-slavery movement while Grandpa Vic spent his time spoiling his namesake Victoria, whom he called Vicky.

Victor Farthingham was an exciting professional in the way he addressed his responsibilities. While he saw the Mansfield Decree as an important weapon when it came to addressing slavers, he had not had the opportunity to apply its edicts. Slavers had made a concerted effort to stay away from his seaport community. Farthingham's only contact to date had come from storm-driven or damaged slave ships.

Major Smith entered Mr. Farthingham's office to alert him that a ship was approaching their port. Immediately Farthingham had the assembly bell rung that set his staff in motion. It would take the unidentified ship a half an hour to come close enough to be identified, but it would only take fifteen minutes for their port to meet and respond to any categories of need the arriving ship might require.

Major Cordell Smith was a marine's marine, a twenty-year veteran of military service to the Empire. Cordell Smith gained his fame during the Seven Years War in Montreal, The Battle of Lagos, The Battle of Quiberon Bay, and the capture of Havana. He was now in his late thirties, married with two small children, and was enjoying his assignment as major of the port garrison. He had been able to departmentalize his war experience and hang it on the wall of his mind like a picture. His philosophy was: "It happened, it is a part of me, I recognize my military service, but I do not allow it to be-all and end-all of my existence." By doing this, Cordell Smith was able to grow spiritually with God, which allowed Major Cordell Smith to enjoy a loving and peaceful existence with his family.

Now he had to reengage his professional persona to address the approaching vessel. The garrison under his command was brought to attention, and every man was at his duty station ready to address any concerns related to the ship approaching that could now be identified as the *Phoenix,* a notorious slave ship captained by an equally notorious captain named Robert Stubbs.

Major Smith still had one last picture from his military service to hang on that mental wall in his mind, the Siege of Fort St. Philip or, as it's known in London, The Fall of Minorca. The most brutal defeat experienced by the British and Major Smith during their conflict with the French. The two men that he held most responsible for the defeat was Admiral John Bying and Robert Stubbs. The British government had administered proper justice to Admiral Bying by introducing him to a firing squad and executing him. Robert Stubbs had vanished into the sinister world of slave trading. And now he was here!

Major Smith had informed Mr. Farthingham of their pending visitor and the human cargo it was carrying. Victor Farthingham, the dockmaster, proceeded to contact the local "Society for Poor Blacks" (SPB). "The Society for Poor Blacks" (SPB) was a national organization committed to ending slavery and to improving the position of "Poor Blacks" in England. The local chapter had been preparing for this day for years. They had spent their time studying and visiting other local chapters to enhance the "dos" and minimize the "don'ts." SPB was ready and waiting. Elder Albert McFall, a local merchant and trader, had gifted the Society for Poor Blacks with a huge warehouse that could meet the needs of hundreds of African captives. Housing, feeding, medical, acclimation, and job securing were all parceled out in the Cathedral of Freedom; that's what they called the warehouse. The whole chapter was now on standby; they had summoned several of the African Londoners who would assist with translation, and they had enough clothing to clothe nearly a thousand people of all sizes. The vice chairperson of the Sussex County Chapter of The Society for Poor Blacks would lead this endeavor, Esther Farthingham-Sancho, the dockmaster's daughter.

Once the *Phoenix* was berthed, Esther's Society for Poor Blacks' Fitness Team would initiate their first involvement. They would assess the health of the passengers and proceed to disembark the Africans based on their ability to ambulate or their need of support. The Society for Poor Blacks' Refresh Team then would provide them the ability to wash and receive clothing plus help them with maintenance of sores and cuts. Their first week would be spent in restoration, rest, and, where possible, reunification. Elder McFall was already working on a celebration for the new Brits in a fortnight. "English air is too pure for a slave to breathe" and the members of the Society for Poor Blacks were going to prove it!

The *Phoenix* slipped quietly into its berth, permitting the moans and stench of its human cargo to permeate the atmosphere of the dock. Captain Stubbs had prepared himself to try bribing with money and loot which might influence these sleepy port officials to take a "blind eye" to his cargo and look the other way while he restocked and left for Jamaica. He was rehearsing his presentation while walking down the gang plank when he saw a detachment of marines approaching. Glistening in their bright red uniforms, they moved with the precision of one.

There was something about the officer leading them that made him snap to attention as if he was amidst certain danger. The officer's gait was familiar to Stubbs but not the silhouette, which was approaching at a rapid rate. Captain Stubbs had not experienced such consternation and rapid heart pace since his military service for the Crown.

The silhouette turned into an image of fear and terror from years gone by, Lieutenant Cordell Smith! Stubbs' last encounter with Smith had Stubbs looking straight down the barrel of Smith's pistol.

Their eyes meet in a harsh, arid way that made it clear that neither man wanted to be in association with the other. Stubbs knew that any attempt to dislodge a compromise from this now Major Smith would be futile. He was hoping that this encounter would not cost him his life or a lengthy prison sentence. Major Smith immediately informed Captain Stubbs of his position and role. He continued by making it clear that if any contraband or slaves were found on the *Phoenix* it would be detained until further notice. There was nothing Stubbs could do or say; he just wanted an end to this encounter as quickly as possible.

Major Smith and his detachment entered the ship cutting through the stench of death and human filth to find four hundred and seventy (470) captured human beings. He immediately had all crew members detained until further notice. He then had Esther and her Fitness Team with a group of African interpreters board the vessel. Esther and Major Smith were amazed by the absence of infants. The Fitness team led the African women and girls off the *Phoenix* and began their renewing.

Rehema left the *Phoenix* in a total state of confusion but with the assurance from the Bantu interpreter that these were good and caring Clear People. She also told Rehema that they were here to help her overcome the nightmare of her capture and the Middle Passage. This was a strange concept for Rehema to accept, the same people who had extended this apocalyptical nightmare into the life of her family were now going to bring her comfort. She then realized that if people who called themselves Africans and looked like her could initiate this hellish living nightmare, then it was possible that there were good, caring Clear People. She would find out if this was true for herself, but if it was not, then she would be prepared to address it, to the death!

Flashes of red raced all around Masego and the other captives, with men shouting in the Bantu dialect: "Don't be alarmed; they are here to help!" The flashes of red evolved into Clear Men dressed as red warriors. As they took their positions amongst the captives; the interpreters told them that they were here to set them free. A strange thought to most, but Masego just started to praise God. He didn't know how God did it, but the madness was being brought to an end, and it would be over soon!

The Society for Poor Blacks Unification Committee began its work three days after the captives had arrived. The committee headed by Herbert Dills and Irma Bixby had the task of identifying those individuals that were married, the name of their spouse, the last time they saw their spouse, and if they knew whether their spouse was on this ship, etc. The men's and women's barracks were at either ends of the Cathedral of Hope, which made casual contact between the males and females impossible.

Elder Albert McFall had commissioned and paid for an acclimation house called the "Hall of the Risen Savior" where Squire Ted Eidson was responsible for directing the preparatory efforts of the Society for Poor Blacks for the Africans. The Hall of the Risen Savior allowed married couples and families to reunite and become familiar with their surroundings and the British way of life. The functions conducted at the Hall of the Risen Savior were vital to these families' ability to participate and blend into British society. Squire Eidson was a caring man who had come to grips with the notion of change and acceptance of others, not because he was struck with a lightning bolt, but because of a lifetime of growth in his relationship with God. Squire Ted, as he liked for everyone to call him, could be quite cantankerous as a facade but showed love and concern for those placed under his tutelage. He had already begun making transferable relationships for employment and housing in London for those Africans ready to venture on and to assist their assimilation into British life.

Once Masego was off the *Phoenix*, he was able to wash and regain his ambulatory skills. After a few days or so he was sent to a room where members of the Refresh Team had assembled. Masego, now comfortable with his surroundings and these Clear People, instructed the interpreter to inform them that he understood their language but had never spoke it. The committee was amazed at this revelation! They began to ask him questions in English and he would answer in Bantu, which would be interpreted by the translator.

Astonished not only by his understanding of English but by his deportment given what he had been through, the Refresh Team made Masego and Rehema the first family to be placed at the Hall of the Risen Savior. There was just something special about this couple that the Refresh Team could not put their finger on!

Masego had one task and one task only. He had to reunite with Rehema and share in her healing process. They had informed Rehema that Masego had survived the journey and was well. He had been spending every waking moment asking about her welfare.

Their reunion at the Cathedral of Hope was truly remarkable. Minutes went by with the couples just being lost in each other's embrace. The sniffles and tears of joy consumed the first ten minutes of their reunion. Masego pulled away from Rehema because he knew it was time to talk about their child, Chipo. He sat Rehema down and eased his chair in front of her. Masego began explaining to her how he had learned their language in order to rescue his family, her, and Chipo. He took her hands, gently caressing them, and explained to her his discovery of what was happening to her and his intended response to it. He kissed her and told her that everything, the abuse and disrespect she had been through, did not diminish his love for her. She fell into his arms, and he embraced her in what was needed, a hug of protection and security. Time couldn't limit their embrace. When they finally emerged from it, they prayed and thanked God for their restoration that has made them even stronger together than before.

Masego rose up from his chair and wandered toward the window. He was now preparing to share what happened to Chipo with Rehema. As he was looking dazed while trying to sort words to express the anguish he was feeling, Rehema came quietly up on him from behind. She hugged him deeply and softly said: "I know that Chipo is dead." He spun around as if he had been stung by a hornets' nest. Before he could say a word, Rehema started to explain how she and the other women were informed about their infants.

Major Smith and Mr. Farthingham had spent hours interrogating and debriefing Captain Stubbs. Their concern centered around the absence of small children on the *Phoenix*. Stubbs informed them that dysentery had killed many of the infants on the beach and that a decision was made by the owner of the holding pens to kill the remaining children and incinerate their bodies on the beach. Captain Stubbs wanted to be extremely clear about where these events happened and that he and his ship had nothing to do with it. On obtaining this information, Esther Farthingham-Sancho met one on one with each mother individually to inform them about what happened to their child.

Hearing Rehema's report on their child's death caused Masego to collapse into her arms as if a three-hundred-pound boulder had been lifted off his back. Masego was sobbing uncontrollably as Rehema consoled him.

During their time at the Cathedral of Hope, Masego's and Rehema's, emotional, mental, physical, and spiritual wounds incurred by this entire journey had been cleansed. Because of the cleansing, through their submission to the "Will of God" for their lives, every hurt caused by this horrific experience was being moved into the healing process. Once that had started, it was time for Masego and Rehema to begin to move forward.

At this point Masego was very proficient in speaking what the Clear People called English. Masego diligently conveyed the knowledge of this new language to his wife Rehema, who was excited about his accomplishment. They worked diligently on becoming proficient in English day and night. They became so good communicating in English that when it was time for them to move to the Hall of the Risen Savior, better known as the "Hall," Squire Ted asked them to assist in teaching English to those residing in the "Hall." Squire Ted explained to them that they would receive a wage for the hours they spent teaching others.

Well, this sparked a series of inquisitive looks between Rehema and Masego. They spoke politely amongst themselves trying to figure out what "wage" meant. Masego thought it must be some kind of special food for being "in service," but Rehema just gave him that assertive look that only a wife could give a husband that was instructing him to "Ask" instead of "Speculating." So he did. Squire Ted explained that wages were money received for rendering a service. He went on to show them what money looked like and explain how it was used in British society.

It immediately became clear to Rehema and Masego that money in England was just as important as their hunting weapons in Africa. This "money" was to be kept!

The first task of Squire Ted and his staff at the "Hall of the Risen Savior" was suggesting that the Africans change their name to names that would be more acceptable to the British ear and to the British population in general. This would greatly assist their desire to accomplish their goal of becoming productive members of British society.

Rehema and Masego, as with many of the Africans, thought this was a troubling proposition. To them, it felt like they were abandoning their families, their heritage, their tribal traditions, and their ancestors. To them, this would require great prayer. The guidance they received from praying was, ***"Respect your past, but prepare to build for your future."***

There would be a lot of accepting new ways to daily life and the replacement of a lifestyle that they could never return to. Masego and Rehema, with the clarity they needed, entered the Hall of the Risen Savior ready to learn what was necessary to build a future in this new land called England. Their thirst for knowledge was only limited by the number of hours in a day. They had learned that the Clear People called themselves White people or Caucasians and called them the Africans, Negroes, or Blacks. They also became aware of what the slave trade was about and its economic purpose. While learning about it was a sickening, experiencing it as they did was even worse. The amazing thing was how clearly "Divine Intervention" had directly interceded for them. Their faith was justified in God, and they would be forever grateful, no matter what they might have to go through for the rest of their lives.

They were getting used to the itchy coverings that were called clothes, a major necessity given England's cold climate. They quickly learned that their primary skill of hunting was not particularly practical in England. England depended on farming and herding for its food supply. Neither of which interested them. They did learn that successful individuals practiced what was called business. Business was where you provide services or goods to somebody else and receive money for what you provided. They also learned that those with the most money where determined to be the most important people in their community.

Rehema and Masego knew that they could use their ability to teach English and translate to make money. Their major concern was determining which village they would reside in and build their family in England. Their trips with Squire Ted had revealed English villages too large to their liking. The places they called cities in England were extremely large but provided the best opportunity to provide services to other people. Even with this dilemma, compared to what they had been through, they saw it more as an opportunity than a hinderance. They were learning, growing, and adjusting to the "English Way of Life."

The matter of whether they would change their name had been resolved by them. They wanted a name that had great meaning and would reaffirm their status in this world. They chose **Harry Freeman for Masego and Kate Freeman for Rehema**. They had decided to inform Squire Ted when they met with him on Friday.

Harry Freeman and Kate Freeman were now ready to go forth to achieve their goals in British life.

6

A BRITISH LIFE for US

Harry and Kate Freeman were now ready for this "New World"! Kate and Harry spent two months teaching English and translation at the Hall of the Risen Savior. Every pence they earned at the Hall was saved in a canvas bag they called "Kuvumilia na Kufanikiwa," "Endure and Achieve." This bag would be the keeper of dreams. If this "New World" that they had been thrusted into by God was governed by money, and if their status in their village was now going to be determined by money, then they would have plenty of it.

It appeared that effort and endurance were the key elements to achieving money. Harry and Kate had been hunters in Africa, which encompassed all those qualities and then some.

Squire Ted had contacted Thomas Walkin, an old friend from his military days. Thomas and Ted had been friends for over thirty years, and Thomas possessed the same mindset that Squire Ted had of the inculcation of Africans into British society. They were both extremely active in the Society for Poor Blacks, and Thomas had been an integral part of the *Somerset v. Stewart* court case that rendered the Mansfield Decree.

After the two men had broken bread and talked about their families and grandchildren, Squire Ted told him at the Hall of the Risen Savior there was an astounding African couple that he felt was prepared to move into the London area. Thomas was amazed by what Ted was telling him. He had not been acquainted with an African couple presenting such a strong understanding of their new existence in Britain. Squire Ted planned for Harry and Kate to meet with Thomas Walkin.

The lunch was an enjoyable experience for the Freemans. Mr. Walkin concluded that the Freemans would be the perfect couple to introduce to the London populace and suggested they spend the next few days in the area. Thomas explained what they had to look forward to in the London area and what it was like living in a large city. He offered Harry a job delivering coal and confirmed that their housing would be in a Society for Poor Blacks' "Growth House" near St. Paul's Cathedral.

This led Harry and Kate to feel comfortable to broach a subject they only conversed about in private. These good

White people wore crosses around their necks, just like the evil White people that had disrupted their lives. They were confused. At both the Cathedral of Hope and The Hall of the Risen Savior, members of the Society for Poor Blacks began sharing their spiritual beliefs they called Christianity. While the Africans appreciated their efforts, their association with those evil Clear People was too fresh of an experience for them to have any interest in their spiritual values. Now it was time.

Thomas Walkin was also a deacon at St. Paul's Cathedral and was eager to share with the Freemans. Thomas started with his belief and the belief of his Christian family in one God. This made Kate and Harry very happy because their Bantu belief was in the belief of one God. Thomas went on to explain the story of the Messiah and how the Messiah provided the guidance to transverse this world controlled by the devil and his demons. This began to excite the Freemans; it was as if it was the continuation of their Bantu beliefs. Mr. Walkin then shared the most important job the Father gave the Messiah, his son, was to die to redeem all human beings if they were willing. Kate was excited about this Messiah, exclaiming that he sounded like a great man. Thomas smiled and stated that the Messiah, whose name is Jesus Christ, was more than a great man, but he would leave that discussion to deacon James Somerset at the weekly Bible study they would be attending.

Harry and Kate were willing to forgo the extensive questions they still had until these "Bible studies" at St. Paul's Cathedral.

The Freemans went back to the Hall to prepare for their move to the London area. After their luncheon visit with Thomas Walkin, they spent three days in the London area. They learned the route that Harry would be using to deliver coal and visited the "Growth House" where they would be staying. Their biggest surprise came from meeting Deacon James Somerset. He was an African just like them! This made the prospect of participating in his Bible study class more interesting. Though he had no familiarity neither with the Bantu language nor African customs, he was clearly an African.

As they were traveling to their new life, Kate told Harry that they would be able to better advance their goals if they worked together. Harry totally agreed with her and suggested that she develop a skill that was acceptable to British culture for British women. Kate snapped to attention, developed a cold dangerous glare, and coldly told Harry in Bantu: "If using the name 'Kate' is going to cause you to forget who 'Rehema' is, then I'll never use the name 'Kate' again!"

Harry realized that he was treading on what these Brits called "thin ice," so he immediately apologized and meekly asked her to proceed with her thoughts. After a moment to dissipate the rage that had overtaken her, she proceeded to explain to him that she was going to work with him delivering coal. Harry was initially startled but quickly composed himself to avoid the "Wrath of Rehema."

Kate continued with her plan. She would dress as a man and learn the intricacies of the job. Working together, they would be able to complete his route in half the time, making it possible for Harry to request an additional route. By doing this, they would be able to secure twice as much money for every day they worked. Kate explained how this would help them to achieve their goals. Harry agreed to Kate's plan while enjoying the revitalization of his wife, his hunting partner, his warrior, the woman that he loved. He knew now that there was nothing Harry and Kate Freeman couldn't accomplish.

The Freemans accepted their responsibility with great enthusiasm. Kate initially covered her hair and wore men's clothing not to offend English sensitivities about what women could do or how they must dress. After a short period of time, because of the Freemans' thoroughness in the function and delivery of services, Kate could be Kate without any concern about her decorum or appearance. Everyone was asking to be placed on the Freemans' routes. Harry and Kate's routes were the epitome of spotless service; you would never know that their coal wagons had been there. While the Freemans' coal delivery services were booming, their interest in staying in a place like London was waning.

They had been attending church services and Bible study at St. Paul's and were enjoying the knowledge and fellowship offered by the St. Paul's family. They had developed a personal relationship with their Sunday school teacher and mid-week Bible study teacher Mr. James Somerset.

Harry and Kate found out that Deacon Somerset, an African, was a key principle in the Mansfield Decree that made it possible for Harry and Kate to secure their freedom. Deacon Somerset had help them to better comprehend some of the understandings in the Bible that are only enlightened by spending serious time with God and in studying the Bible.

There were several things that Deacon Somerset helped clarify. Specifically, the questions Harry and Kate had about the relationship and connections between their Beliefs in one God from Africa and the Christian Beliefs in One God in England.

Harry did not understand how One God could be the same God in three Individual entities at the same time. Deacon Somerset smiled and stated that the Bible provided the foundation to growing in understanding in one verse. He proceeded to tell them that human beings often confuse themselves by seeking answers to the unanswerable, while ignoring the treasures of God through their lack of "Obedience and Patience," which impacted their studying and growth in "God's Word." He further intimated to Harry and Kate, to grow properly God's Way, you must first accept Deuteronomy 29th Chapter, the 29th verse. He then offered this version, "The Lord our God has secrets known to no one. We are not accountable for them, but we and our children are accountable forever for all that he has revealed to us, so that we may obey all the terms of these instructions." [NLT]

Kate and Harry thought that this would be very beneficial in growing their relationship with God. Deacon Somerset, however, knew they needed some understanding of the "Trinity." James started by stating that, "Now that you are familiar with 'Ice,' you know that one complete glass of water can become three distinct entities, 'Ice, Steam, and Liquid.'" He furthered elaborated that confusion settles into individuals' spirits by trying to figure out "How" God does what He does instead of "Why." James then told them that the first member of the Trinity, God the Father, always remains a "Spirit" that man cannot gaze upon and live.

The second member of the Trinity, the Son, His Old Testament duties as the "Word" were to be a part of everything made by the Father. Then His second job, in the Old Testament, required Him to take on flesh as "The Angel of the LORD" and provide warnings, instructions, and guidance.

Then there was a four-hundred-year period where there was no "Word" from God. Harry and Kate were enthralled with what James was sharing, and they were beginning to learn how to read with the help of the staff at the Growth House using the Bible. Deacon Somerset enhanced their development with his extensive library that brought Kate and Harry great joy. After a small tea break, they resumed their conversation about the Trinity.

James started by sharing the Son's duties in the New Testament. His first goal as the Messiah, carrying the name Jesus the Christ, was to surrender his life on the cross to give all mankind the free gift of salvation. His second goal was to provide to all mankind a step-by-step guide to overcome our freewill and become more obedient to God's Will for our life.

The third member of the Trinity, the Holy Spirit, finally made it possible for every human being to have a direct conversation and relationship with God the Father. They no longer had to wait for a Holy man or woman to get a word or directions from God the Father.

Kate and Harry found their conversation with Deacon Somerset very stimulating. They were convinced that their traditional beliefs and these new Christian points of beliefs where similar, and now with a better understanding of the Trinity, it became acceptable. For them, the Bible amplified what they had been taught back home in Africa.

The Freemans' coal delivery business was working well for the industrious couple. Their assimilation into British culture was seamless, and before too long, they had moved out of the "Growth House" and had secured their own apartment. They were adjusting to urban life, but it wasn't their first choice of lifestyles. It was hard for them to understand why people would want to live so tightly packed together. It clearly made communal hygiene more difficult and privacy nearly impossible away from your apartment. The one factor that made it extremely clear to them that city life was not for them was their food. They were hunters, and the meat that was offered in the city was closer to spoiled than fresh, and the vegetables were old and questionable.

Even with these questionable negatives, their freedom quenched these concerns and put a smile on Kate and Harry's faces, although they could appreciate the addition of more sunny days. James Somerset became close friends with the Freemans. Their conversations not only centered on religious doctrine but also their personal lives and how they had arrived in England.

Harry and Kate shared every aspect and detail of their life in Africa, their capture, and the Middle Passage with

James. James was amazed at the life that Harry and Kate shared in Africa. He was startled to believe that such a small handful of White people could capture so many warriors and their families. It seemed impossible for those Europeans to have such a devastating impact on so many Africans.

Harry smiled and looked James deep in the eyes and told him that if it was only White people attempting to displace them from their homes, the few that escaped death would be running across the water back to Europe. James laughed and asked Harry: "So what happened in making them so successful in capturing you?" Harry replied with a sullen stern look, "Other Africans! They would have never been able to herd us like cattle if it wasn't for envious tribes with leaders like Chief Apunda." Harry's voice became sharp, and his eyes filled with anger as he continued, "They would have never abused our wives and girls and killed our children without the help of people who look like us!" James could see the anger that still gripped Harry's spirit. He turned to Harry with a look of understanding and compassion and said to Harry, "Until you forgive those that did you wrong, it will curtail the growth of your future; it will act like a continuous bad toothache in your life. Even worse and more important, if you do not forgive others, God cannot forgive you of your sins."

Kate held Harry, and Harry embraced Kate; they were sobbing together. Sobs turned into screams and a releasing of feelings and emotions that had been boarding in their minds and hearts since their capture, rent free. A shedding of tangible deep feelings that they had been protecting and safeguarding in order to keep the other from hurt and pain. They heard God telling them, "Let it Go; Let it Go. It's taking up space in your mind and life that I have reserved for greater things."

While the Freemans where deep in, what looked like to Deacon Somerset, an encounter with the Lord, he proceeded to walk outside and took a seat on the step. He knew what was happening. It was "God's Cleansing." It had happened to him after he had been set free. It was the great purge of what fellow human beings had done to them based on their evil, malicious, and hurtful desires spurred on by their individual and collective "freewill."

Somerset was having his ongoing discussion with the Lord. His directions were clear as his role with Harry and Kate. He was to explain what the end game of the Middle Passage was like and what a life as a slave was synonymous to. He was to explain the predominate type of settlers in the New World, known as the colonies, and what their primary goal was. The Lord instructed him on the primary difference between the Northern colonies and the Southern colonies. Deacon Somerset was to guide them back to the "hell on Earth" that he himself had emerged from for people of color, the British colonies of America.

After what seemed like an eternity, Kate and Harry emerged from their "Gathering with God," as they would call it. The Freemans would learn that their "Gathering with God" would always bring them the clarity they would need to confront needs and situations God's Way and move forward.

Holding each other with a look of renewal in their eyes, Harry and Kate found the clarity and comfort they needed. James heard them stirring, so he arose from his "Gathering with God" and reentered the house, realizing the approach he must take to advance God's Will.

Kate smiled and informed James that she was going to start preparing their midday meal and for Harry and himself to take a walk to the local vendors and secure a few items she needed for lunch. The men eagerly took advantage of this opportunity and proceeded accordingly. During their walk to the vendors, Harry turned to James and was attempting to apologize for their earlier outburst of emotions. James interrupted Harry mid-sentence and informed him that was how God works to prepare us for what's next according to His Will. James shared with Harry that while he and Kate were going through their cleansing with the Lord; the Lord was guiding him in his next step with them. James felt very comfortable in sharing what the Lord had equipped him to share with Harry and Kate. James told Harry they would discuss it with them after lunch. He said, "Let's get Kate her requested items, but first, let's make a slight detour to a dessert vendor I know!" Deacon Somerset's excitement was that of a school-aged boy, and it puzzled Harry. Harry was not yet accustomed to this British notion of dessert.

In Africa there was an abundance of honey, fruits, and berries to satisfy what the English people called a "sweet tooth." In England they depended on funny-looking bowls and plates of things combined and blended to the point that they were unrecognizable called desserts. Harry and Kate had artfully avoided having to digest these things called desserts, that appeared to totally mutilate fruits and berries, at the gatherings they had been to since coming to England. Now was going to be the moment of truth. Harry was going to walk into his home with an arm full of desserts. He knew what Kate's inner reaction would be, but he also knew that Kate and himself loved their friend and mentor Deacon James Somerset. So, today the Freemans would have their first experience with a British dessert.

Harry and James were entering a part of the city that Harry had never been to before. Down an alley they went till they reached a little shop with a bright sign that said, "Tuttle's Bakery." Inside was a cheerful rosy-cheeked lady named Mrs. Tuttle, the proprietor. She greeted them with a boisterous Cockney hello and gave Deacon Somerset a hardy shaking of the hand and a "God Bless You!" James introduced Harry to Mrs. Tuttle, and she extended the same hardy handshake and "God Bless You" to him.

Harry was familiar with the British custom of shaking hands, but this was the first time he feared his arm might become detached from his body. He had heard about how down to earth Cockneys were, and he was enjoying it. He surmised that this was the ultimate greeting of excitement and joy. Deacon Somerset informed Mrs. Tuttle that he would like to purchase a rhubarb pie and six Shrewsbury cakes. Mrs. Tuttle gathered their requested items and James paid for the desserts, but Mrs. Tuttle had a surprise for her first-time visitor Harry. She handed Harry a little bag with two lardy cakes and said, "You and the Mrs. enjoy these with your tea in the morning."

On the walk back home, Harry shared with James Kate and his desire to escape the city lifestyle. He told James that they felt stifled and inhibited from being who they really were. Wow, James thought to himself, it was amazing how God works! He had been groping with how to broach the subject that God had laid before him with the Freemans and now Harry had given him an open portal for their conversation after lunch.

As they continued to walk and Harry continued to share, James smiled with a nod of agreement here and there.

Kate was in the midst of preparing her midday feast when Harry and James had returned. She told them to wash up and make themselves comfortable because lunch would be served in less than thirty minutes.

Lunch was an epicurean delight. Kate had become an excellent cook and believed in cooking with flavor which required plenty of spices. To their amazement, they truly enjoyed the British desserts. Harry was so enthralled with the rhubarb pie that he asked Kate to get a recipe and learn how to bake one; Kate smiled and nodded politely.

Deacon Somerset reconvened their conversation in the parlor as he begin by telling them about what it was like being a slave in the colonies. He explained to them that everything associated with slavery was geared to dehumanize you and destroy any sense of family and relationships. James provided a detailed view and summation of his life in the colonies. Harry and Kate were startled at James accounting of cruelty, subjugation, and servitude for the sake of money. James continued with the story of how he had obtained his freedom and how that had produced the Mansfield Decree which basically said no new slaves in England, which gave the Freemans their freedom. Kate fell to her knees and began praising God. She looked up at James and Harry and said, "This is all by God's design that we are here in England together."

Deacon Somerset shouted, "Absolutely!" He furthered explained that during his "Gathering with God," he was instructed to share with them about the "New World." He started by explaining that the colonialists were mostly escaping something, and if not governed by the dictates and edicts of God, they had very little concern or compassion towards Africans. He told them that the colonies could provide an African some opportunities in the Northern colonies but definitely not in the Southern colonies.

He told them in the South their freedom would mean nothing and that they would be exposed to many devious attempts to place them in slavery. He suggested that they pray about going to the New World but explore being indentured servants in the northern colonies of the "New World." James explained to Harry and Kate what indentured servitude meant. Indentured Servitude was the process by which an individual in the colonies would pay your fare to the New World and you would agree to pay off your fare over a defined amount of years by working for that individual. He said when they had made their minds up, he would put them in touch with Wilbur Rhondenham. Deacon Somerset informed them that Wilbur was currently a Deacon at St. Paul's Cathedral who was heading up the Church's Indentured Servant Assistance Program and, as a professional, owned an agency that handled travel needs for the general citizenry. The conversation continued as they raised questions about just beginning to adjust to British life in England, and now, if they pursued "Indentured Servitude," it would be another transitional period for the Freemans.

They finished their festivities, polishing off the rhubarb pie and Shrewsbury cakes and wished Deacon Somerset well as he was departing. They had a myriad of concerns to contemplate and present before God for clarity. They were interested in everything that James Somerset said about the New World. They could envision functioning in that environment and how it could be very beneficial to the development of their goals for the Freeman family. Harry and Kate's only concern was being confronted with the expected racism in the colonies. There was no doubt in their minds that residency in the Southern colonies was totally out of the question.

They went into prayer and petition to God for direction. They were still waiting on clarity from the Father when it was time to resume their work routine. Harry and Kate walked to the coal depot, secured their horses and wagons, and loaded their coal, then proceeded on their individual routes. During her deliveries, Kate had a "Gathering with God." God brought back to her remembrance the sermon Rev. Beilby Porteus gave at church a few weeks ago. She couldn't remember the name of the sermon, but she remembered what it was about.

She summarized the sermon like this:

Jesus was with his apostles, and he told them, "We must go over to the other side." Jesus and the twelve apostles got in the boat and started across the lake. Halfway across they encountered a bad storm that scared the apostles. Being scared, they woke Jesus up. Jesus chastised them for having such little Faith and said to the storm, "Peace, be still," and the storm ceased. The apostles where amazed at the fact that the wind and rain obeyed his command.

Kate thought that was amazing, but God was showing her something else. Yes, the wind and the rain obeyed his command, but there was no need to be scared in the first place because Jesus said, "We have to go across," and he was in the boat with them! The Lord said to her, "If I am with you, there is nothing to worry about. Go across, I'll be with you."

That evening Kate talked to Harry about her "Gathering with God." She explained to him how the Almighty had brought her to remembrance of Rev Beilby Porteus's sermon a few weeks prior. Harry was well aware of the contents of that sermon because Rev Porteus was one of Harry's favorite preachers, and he would never miss an opportunity to hear one of his sermons when he came to preach at St. Paul's. Kate explained that the Lord would be with them, in the ship, and that they had to go across to achieve God's Will for their life.

Harry turned away from Kate and walked slowly from her with his head down and slightly shaking his head with no purpose. When his slow sauntering ended abruptly, Harry, not looking, placed his hands high on the wall and slapped the palm of his hand against it several times. He turned, and there was an elongated pause as he looked at Kate that elicited concern from her. She started to approach him out of concern because she had not experienced this behavior from him before. As she approached him getting ready to inquiry about his well-being, Harry interrupted her and said, "We'll contact Wilbur Rhondenham tomorrow."

Harry and Kate, after Sunday church service, asked Deacon Somerset to introduce them to Deacon Rhondenham. James was more than happy to honor their request. The three searched for him in the throng of church goers laughing and socializing. After thirty minutes and no luck, James told the Freemans that he would get in touch with Wilbur and inform him of their interest.

The walk home was a little slower and a little sullen because their expectations did not match their reality. They had wanted to meet Wilbur Rhondenham, consummate their business, and be on their way to the New World immediately. By the time they reached their home, they had reached the conclusion that God was instilling in them the "Acceptance of Patience." If they were going to survive in the New World, "Patience" would have to become their best friend. Three weeks had passed before they heard from James Somerset again. Deacon Somerset had not attended church service over the past weeks.

Harry and Kate took it in stride and had not pursued the whereabouts of either Deacon Somerset or Deacon Rhondenham. They were learning "Everything in God's Time." "Patience" was starting to move into their lives; Harry and Kate were starting to accept the fact "that God does not set His Clock by our pocket watch." This delay in the Freeman's desired timing had turned into a true blessing which allowed them to address some of the small items they had overlooked. It seemed that Deacon Rhondenham had gone on holiday and James had to depart to the city of Ely to deliver a speech and participate in discussions and a conference on the immorality of slavery for The Society for Poor Blacks. Kate and Harry were happy to see James and to know he was well. James was delighted to see them and told them they would meet Deacon Rhondenham at his home after church next Sunday at dinner.

The week flew by with the Freemans excited about moving forward on their new life. Rev Beilby Porteus delivered a stirring sermon about showing the love of Christ by how we treat the poor and strangers. After service Kate and Harry greeted Rev Porteus, and he and Harry began talking about the subtle nuances of his sermon. As their discussion continued, James walked up with Wilbur Rhondenham, made the proper introductions, and reminded them that he would see them at his home around 5:00. Rev Porteus was the first to nod to the affirmative. What a welcome surprise to Harry and Kate; they did not realize that he would be joining them for dinner at the Somerset home.

Harry and Kate hurried home to freshen up and to bring the rhubarb pie they bought from Mrs. Tuttle's bakery for dessert. They had found themselves spending a great deal of time at Mrs. Tuttle's shop just to enjoy her Cockney stories and enjoy her dialect. It just seemed so alive to the Freemans.

When Kate and Harry arrived, everybody was sitting in the parlor conversing. The aromas wafting from the kitchen were a cacophony of coordinated sensual delights, orchestrated by the maestro of culinary delight herself, Jillian Somerset.

Jillian Somerset, James's wife, had prepared a lamb roast with brown gravy, potatoes, carrots, and Brussel sprouts. The meal was delicious, and the conversation was even better. It started with Freemans being questioned and quizzed about going to the "New World." Rev Porteus and Wilbur Rhondenham were particularly concerned about their reaction to racist attitudes in the colonies. Wilbur shared stories of how he had to intervene in behalf of many White Indentured Servants, particularly people of Irish descent in the colonies with mixed results but for the few African Indentured Servants that he had assisted, his pleas for justice and equality fell on deaf ears.

Kate and Harry looked at each other and started to share with them their most intimate details of their life in Africa, their capture, the loss of Chipo and the voyage that brought them to England. They even explained the pain and trauma they experienced in England every time they saw a "guinea sack." Harry explained how it got its name, based on where the people being enslaved were from, and what it was used for, to transport the enslaved infants and small children. Kate informed their friends that every "guinea sack" they saw right there in England, that city, and even their own home, caused them to trip over our own hatred and bitterness. She continued by explaining that even in the midst of them gaining their freedom, meeting, caring, and loving people, rebuilding a life and creating a future there was a river of bitterness and hatred flowing through their minds. Surrendering the names that their parents had given them only added strong currents and rapids to the now growing deadly river of hatred and bitterness that had grown from the stumbling blocks to an impassible obstacle in their minds.

All the time on the outside they were learning, working, and growing to love the unlovable humans, they felt like a melon that looked good on the surface but was all eaten out by worms underneath. Until God brought to their remembrance the talk Major Cordell Smith gave to the group of freed slaves living at the "Hall of the Risen Savior."

Major Smith had talked about the trauma and distress he had accumulated from years of being a soldier and how it was destroying his life and his relationship with his family. He said, "You must surrender your hate and bitterness to God, then you can heal and grow and obtain the inner peace that every human being needs."

Major Smith then explained how he took those stumbling blocks and obstacles of hate and bitterness and put them one by one in God's Picture Frame of "Love Anyhow" and hung them on the "walls of his mind."

Major Cordell Smith's exact words were, "Just like a picture in your home, you know it's there, you've acknowledged its impact, but you don't dwell on it all day.

But you must have the bitterness and hatred placed in God's Picture Frame of 'Love Anyhow.' What will keep the picture from falling off the wall is your willingness to use 'Spiritual Nails.' Spiritual Nails say, 'If you do not forgive others of their sins, then God will not forgive you of your sins.'"

Kate told their friends that after God had reminded them of Major Smith and his speech, she and Harry asked the Father for a barrel of Spiritual Nails, and they got busy framing and hanging all their hatred and bitterness.

Harry rose and said, "I am Masego, son of Unathi and Femi from the Beti-Pahuin Clan of the Bantu Tribe." Kate rose and said, "I am Rehema, daughter of Rufaro and Chinwe from the Bubi Clan of the Bantu Tribe."

They embraced each other and looked at their friends with a smile and said, "We are the Freemans, Harry and Kate, and we are ready to cross the sea with Christ."

7

A NEW WORLD FOR A NEW PEOPLE

Wilbur set up an appointment for Kate and Harry to meet him an hour before Bible studies on Wednesday. Kate and Harry were there early on Wednesday. Their resolve and perseverance in achieving their goal of reaching the New World was driving their every thought.

Deacon Rhondenham brought them into his office and started with prayer. After prayer, Wilbur's inquiry was about their resolve to make this move to the colonies. They assured him that their commitment to move to the British colonies was rock solid. After Wilbur was comfortable with their assurances of commitment, he began sharing his knowledge of the different colonies and his business associates there.

He shared with Harry and Kate that he felt the province of New York would be the best location for them. New York was still a vast wilderness, suitable for a young couple who wanted to build a family and a future of their own. He told them about the Hardenberghs, whom he had provided a multitude of indentured servants to over the years, even a few Africans. Wilbur told the Freemans that from his last communique from Leonard Hardenbergh his son, John L Hardenbergh, was venturing out on his own and was looking for a young couple who would work and grow with him.

Deacon Rhondenham informed them that he would send a communique to John Hardenbergh telling him about them and how he believed Harry and Kate would be great indentured servants and that they were Black. They were Africans who had gained their freedom through the Mansfield Decree and had achieved remarkable success in assimilating into British society, but they did not care for city life. Wilbur knew that the only stumbling block could be the color of their skin but knowing the Hardenbergh Clan, he was not concerned.

Deacon Rhondenham told Harry and Kate that they would not have a response from Hardenbergh for several weeks depending on the conditions of the Atlantic Ocean. He suggested that Harry and Kate spend the next couple of months getting their affairs in order and saying their goodbyes.

Harry and Kate addressed their goodbyes on a professional level with a little gift to all their customers.

Kate had been spending more time helping and learning from Mrs. Tuttle at her bakery. Mrs. Tuttle had taught Kate how to make Harry's favorite dessert, rhubarb pie. Over the next several weeks, every customer on Harry and Kate's routes received a rhubarb pie with a note of blessings and gratitude from the Freemans. Their personal goodbyes centered around their church family at St. Paul's and their neighbors in their vicinity.

The Freemans were ready to start this new venture; all they needed now was to learn if John L Hardenbergh Jr. was going to pay their fare in exchange for their labor. Wilbur Rhondenham had provided them great detail about the Hardenbergh family but didn't know very much about John Hardenbergh.

Arnoldus van Hardenbergh was the first Hardenbergh to leave Holland in 1644 to emigrate to New Amsterdam. Arnoldus was a merchant and brought with him delicacies from Holland. This garnered him great favor with the people of New Netherlands. Arnoldus van Hardenbergh was an original member of the New Netherland's governing body called "The Nine Men of New Netherland." The Dutch in New Netherland had devised a unique way of governance. The people would choose from their most notable citizens eighteen delegates complied from merchants, farmers, and wealthy bourgeoise, then the director general chose nine men to govern.

Johannes van Hardenbergh was a merchant like his brother and had settled on Manhattan Island. Johannes's good business acumen and concern for the general populace placed him in great honor in the Dutch community in New Netherland, and he was appointed to succeed his brother on "The Nine Men of New Netherland."

The Hardenberghs were men of vision and venture. In 1706 Johannes, along with six other family members, secured a land grant from the British Crown for 1.5 million acres in Northern Ulster County, New York. So, a large portion of the Hardenbergh Clan moved from Manhattan Island to the wilderness of Rosendale in Ulster County.

Two members of the Hardenbergh Clan, who would make this Wilderness Land in Rosendale in the Province of New York an adventurer's and an explorer's delight, would be Johannes's two sons, Johannes Hardenbergh Jr. and J. Leonard Hardenbergh.

Johannes Hardenbergh Jr. had accepted a commission of colonel in the British Colonial Service Army and played an important role in protecting the Wilderness during the French and Indian conflict. Johannes's son Rev. Dr. Jacob R Hardenbergh became the first president of Rutgers College. The family was always looking to expand their horizons.

Leonard Hardenbergh, the younger brother of Johannes, concentrated his efforts on building upon the

Wilderness property that the Hardenberghs already possessed. Leonard was the leader of the hardy yeomanry of Ulster, the British Military Reserve. Leonard was the Hardenbergh that had a personal relationship with Wilbur Rhondenham. Wilbur had sent the Hardenbergh Clan over fifty indentured servants over the last ten years. Now John L. Hardenbergh was ready to begin developing his share of the family's land grant in Rosendale.

When the letter and contract reached Deacon Rhondenham, he immediately contacted Harry and Kate, and the celebrations began. The Freemans expressed their love and appreciation for all that was done for them. Harry and Kate pledged their eternal gratitude to the Society for Poor Blacks with special plaudits to Esther Farthingham-Sancho, Major Cordell Smith, Elder Albert McFall, Squire Ted Eidson, Deacon Wilbur Rhondenham, Rev. Beilby Porteus, and the Somersets, Jillian and James.

Harry and Kate had spent personal time with Deacon James Somerset and his wife, Jillian Somerset. They wanted to express their deep affection for everything they had done for the Freemans. They also wanted to let the Somersets know that there would always be a place for them in the Freemans' home. James was delighted with the affection displayed by the Freemans; he assured them that his experience in the colonies had thwarted and blunted any desire to return to the New

World. Deacon Somerset said he and Jillian would always keep them in their prayers and that they would always be welcomed in their home. They hugged and kissed and shed tears of joy and remorse because of the pending departure.

The trip to the New World was uneventful. They were glad to be off the ocean and to feel firm earth under their feet. The Freemans landed in the largest city of the Province of New York, New York City. The Province of New York was named after King James II's brother James, Duke of York, and after the Third Anglo-Dutch War was truly under English domination.

The Freemans were amazed at the metropolitan nature of the entire area. They were hoping that their new home with John L Hardenbergh in Rosendale Village was far away from New York City, the third biggest city in the British Empire, behind London and Philadelphia.

Waiting for Harry and Kate at the end of the gang plank was a young man with a small sign that said "FREEMANS." Harry and Kate were delighted to have somebody greeting them as they departed the ship. Their initial impression was that this young man must be an employee of Mr. Hardenbergh. To their amazement, the polite young man with the million-dollar smile and persona was Mr. John L Hardenbergh Jr. The man they would be working for and who paid their fare. John greeted them with a smile that exposed his inner soul.

That smile put Harry and Kate at total ease and relieved their fears of this new relationship.

He was extremely energetic and adventurous and was the type of man that was fair with all men. John judged a man by his character and was not big on a lot of wasted verbiage. Action is what drove this man of the frontier. He had stayed close to home to assure that his parents, J. Leonard Hardenbergh and Rachel Hardenbergh, were comfortable since his father had begun to address different ailments. Now that they were situated and had the proper support staff around them, it was time for him to begin to advance his dreams. The Freemans would be the first indentured servants that he would be completely responsible for every aspect of their lives. John L. Hardenbergh Jr. saw this as the most important aspect of his new future, and he prayed to God to provide him proper direction.

John explained to them that Rosendale Village was ninety miles north of New York City and contained none of the hustle and bustle of New York City. Kate and Harry were relieved to hear that tidbit of good news and began to ask Mr. Hardenbergh how he had chosen Rosendale as a place to reside. Before he responded to their question he stated, "My friends and family call me John, and since we are going to become both, call me John." The Freemans nodded and said, "Well, John, why Rosendale?" John L Hardenbergh started by sharing his family's involvement in America.

He started by letting Harry and Kate know that the Hardenberghs have been a very prominent family in colonial history since 1644 as a part of New Amsterdam. Arnoldus van Hardenbergh emigrated from Holland to New Amsterdam in New Netherland in 1644. Arnoldus was a merchant, and he arrived in the New World with a ship load merchandise to sell in New Amsterdam.

Arnoldus became recognized as a prominent member of New Netherland Society because of his skills as a merchant and his concern for the New Amsterdam community. Because of his meticulous efforts to promote the wellbeing of all members of their communal society, Arnoldus van Hardenbergh was appointed to the "Original Nine Men of New Netherland." The Dutch way of governing in the New World was through the Nine Men of New Netherland, which provided advisory advice to the director general. Eighteen delegates were selected by the people from the merchants, bourgeoise, and farmers. The director general would select the "Nine Men" from this grouping.

His brother Johannes van Hardenbergh followed him to New Netherland and succeeded Arnoldus on the "Nine Men of New Netherland." Johannes was a merchant like his brother but was also the visionary in the family. Johannes van Hardenbergh organized a group of six relatives to purchase 1.5 million acres of wilderness land in Northern Ulster County in New York from the British

Crown. His son Johannes Hardenbergh Jr. became a colonel in the English Colonial Service. He was active in the New York Troops for the defense of the frontier against the French and Indians. Johannes van Hardenbergh's grandson, the Rev. Dr. Jacob R Hardenbergh, became the first president of Rutgers College in New Brunswick, NJ. Hardenberghs were true visionaries, and John L Hardenbergh was not going to be out done.

The Hardenberghs' focal point in Northern Ulster County was Rosendale Village. They had picked this vicinity because it contained all the attributes needed to build a stable community. Being of Dutch origin they were quite aware of the role wind and water played in producing the energy necessary to operate mills.

Rosendale Village had the Rondout Creek which was a tributary of the Hudson River flowing through the area, plus the benefits of LeFever Falls. LeFever Falls rushed out of the Joppenbergh Mountain, which was part of the Catskill Mountain Range, providing the Hardenberghs a highly efficient source of energy.

John's father, J Leonard Hardenbergh, had orchestrated the development of the area for the Hardenbergh Clan, and now was now having some health issues. John had spent the last several years addressing needs that his father deemed important; now John was ready to venture out on his own.

John had reconnoitered the Hardenbergh Clan's expansive land holdings. He decided to optimize the resources that were abundantly available and the energy producing waterfalls and rivers in the area of wilderness southwest of the family homestead in Rosendale. The property that was stoking John L Hardenbergh's future visions was about forty miles from his parents' home.

The Hardenbergh Clan knew the potential their huge land grant possessed, but only a few members of the family wanted to address the trials and tribulations of wilderness existence and life. John was going to attack the Wilderness head-on. One of the attributes that Harry and Kate Freeman possessed was that they were Africans and, by nature, would neither be intimidated by life in the Wilderness nor wild animals roaming at night.

As John was sharing his family's history and accomplishments along with his dreams, Kate and Harry were extremely excited. They began to think that this "New World" might be "God's Way" of providing them a "New Take," on their "Old World in Africa." John's discussion about the Wilderness gave them the hope that they would be able to hunt, trap, and fish again and would be able to build homes away from the general population. The Freemans' belief was, the least amount of interaction with people reduced their need to respond to racist attitudes.

It was a three-night and four-day journey to Rosendale Village. Harry and Kate were ecstatic to be in nature again. The Wilderness had many similarities to the bush back home, which excited their remembrance of warm thoughts of Africa. They spent the journey to Rosendale sharing their lives in Africa with John including, their daughter Chipo, their capture, the Middle Passage and the story of their freedom. Most importantly, they shared their commitment to God and how He brought them through everything. Kate and Harry explained to John that their primary duty for their village was to secure bush meat; they were hunters by nature. John L Hardenberg became one of the first White men in the colonies to have a full understanding of Agooji Warriors, Tree Leopards, the Bubi People, the Beti-Pahuin People, and the Bantu Tribe. Harry and Kate even shared their African names with John, Masego and Rehema. John was enthralled with the stories of their lives that Harry and Kate shared with him.

By the time they reached the homestead in Rosendale Village, John knew that God had led him in the right direction by choosing Harry and Kate Freeman. Harry and Kate were introduced to the members of the Hardenbergh family and settled into their quarters and began thanking God for their new life in the New World.

The Freemans spent the next two weeks learning the ins and outs of the Hardenberghs' homestead. They had built a totally efficient society with all types of mills to meet their everyday needs. John, having learned more about Harry and Kate, thought they could assist in a venture he wanted to pursue.

John wanted to explore procuring, salting, and selling meats. He had discovered a salt cavern on the property he wanted to develop, if the Freemans could transport the salt to a processing mill. He planned to build the mill near Verkeerderkill Falls. Harry and Kate would also be responsible for hunting wild game to be processed. Hauling salt and hunting wild game, for Kate and Harry, was like walking and talking at the same time. They had been hunters in Africa, and they delivered coal in England; God could not have prepared them any better for their new life in the colonies. John had introduced the use and care of a rifle to Kate and Harry while traveling to Rosendale Village. Now at the Hardenbergh homestead, daily target practice was a common occurrence. Harry and Kate became very proficient in the use of firearms. Even though they thought it gave them an unfair advantage during the hunt, they appreciated the advantage.

John L Hardenbergh had an expansive area of Wilderness to devote his efforts. The area contained approximately 750 square miles, or 480,000 acres. It stretched from Verkeerderkill Falls in the east, to Peekamoose Mountain in the north, to White Lake in the west, to the ice caves in the south. He knew the Freemans could be an integral part of that vision. He and Harry were contemporaries and shared a considerable amount of likes and dislikes; they were becoming close friends.

The only hinderance to John's future plans resided in the growing political unrest in the colonies. Since the French and Indian War, the Townshend Acts, the Proclamation Act, the Mansfield Decree, the Sugar Act and the Stamp Act, the opposition to British rule of the colonies was growing and was beginning to manifest itself in open aggression.

In the Wilderness, tensions were extremely high between the Native Americans of the Iroquois Confederacy, consisting of six nations of Iroquois-speaking people, the Cayuga, the Mohawk, the Oneida, the Onondaga, the Seneca, and the Tuscarora, and the new settlers in the Northern Wilderness of the Province of New York. The spike in tension between the Iroquois Confederacy, euphemistically called Indians, and the settlers was the Proclamation Act. The settlers were to stay east of the Appalachian Mountains according to the Proclamation Act, but they refused to comply.

The merchants in the Eastern Provinces were up in arms because of taxation and were beginning to sabotage British Empire properties and goods. Notables like Patrick Henry of Virginia and Benjamin Franklin of Pennsylvania, a wealthy printer, were among a long list of orators stoking the "Boilers of Change" for the British colonies against the British Empire.

The Southern Provinces were worried about the British government extending the Mansfield Decree to the colonies, which would destroy their economy built around slavery. A way of life that they were not willing to depart from, no matter how contrary it was to their "Spiritual Beliefs and Values."

The Sugar Act, which placed taxes on everyday items including sugar, the Currency Act, which eliminated colonial governments from issuing their own currency, and the Stamp Act, which placed a tax on all paper used in the colonies, provided the substance necessary to orchestrate, the "Colonies' Harmony of Resistance." All identified by one rhythmic expression "No taxation without Representation!"

John was praying that a peaceful resolution could be worked out, but he was prepared to fight if he must. Plans were already in the works for his uncle Johannes Hardenbergh to head up the Committee of Safety for Ulster County. John shared these concerns with Harry and Kate, and they told him that they would pray for peace, but if it must be war, they were willing and ready to fight.

John had estimated for his meat processing operations he would need four wagon loads of salt per week brought to his processing site near Verkeerderkill Falls. The salt caves were a day's journey from the proposed processing plant. Hardenbergh estimated that the Freemans would take four to five days to deliver the necessary salt and could spend the rest of their time hunting for wild game. He figured the wild game would augment the domestic livestock he would be processing.

John showed Harry and Kate the supplies they would be taking to the new territory. The Freemans inspected the equipment and saw they had everything they needed to build a small settlement of five buildings, from which to live and work, not far from the Verkeerderkill Falls.

Harry informed John that they would require an additional wagon and team of horses. He reminded John that Kate also managed her own coal wagon in England and was quite capable of handling a team and a wagon of salt. Harry had figured out that that he and Kate could deliver the required weekly salt needs in three days. This would allow the Freemans to make an additional delivery of salt and wild game. Harry and Kate would build a salt shelter near the processing building that would contain a surplus of salt that would grow by a wagonload every week. The shelter would contain enough protected salt to meet any situation which might confront John. John was enthralled with Harry's idea. Having a surplus of ready salt opened a whole area of opportunities that he had not thought of before.

Everything was progressing as John Hardenbergh had envisioned. Harry and Kate Freeman had completed three of the five buildings for John's no-name settlement. They had created a nine-wagon surplus of salt that was safely stored in the salt shed. John's processing building was completed. Harry had an uncanny ability to navigate the Wilderness and had become a sharpshooter with the long rifle. Life could not be better for the Freemans and Hardenberghs.

John and Harry had become close friends and spent most of their free time in the Bush Country, as Harry liked to call the Wilderness Country. John was a skilled hunter, but Harry was able to share with him his expertise as an African bush hunter. John was very appreciative of Harry's talents and patience, and they bounded like brothers, with love and respect for each other. The foundation of this relationship was based on their love and obedience to God and His Word in the Bible. This New World had become the "Haven of Their Delight" that Kate and Harry had prayed for and John L Hardenbergh had become the Gem of this Haven. John L Hardenbergh was truly a member of their family.

The news came as a staccato gallop of an overworked horse, driven by a frantic young man needing to deliver urgent concerns. He dismounted before his faithful charge could stop and yelled, "Lieutenant Hardenbergh, Lieutenant Hardenbergh!" John stepped out and calmed the young man down and inquired what would cause him to jeopardize his steed and himself in this manner.

The young man gathered himself and explained that John's uncle, Col. Johannes Hardenbergh, had called for the Committee of Safety for Ulster County to muster in Kingston, Ulster County's chief town and the location of the New York Provincial Congress.

John didn't need any further explanation; he knew that war was eminent. If Uncle John was calling the Committee of Safety together, they were about to become the 2nd New York Militia under General George Clinton. Their responsibility would be the defense of the Hudson River above the Highlands.

Everything was going to have to be put on hold. John told the Freemans what was happening and that they would have to return to the homestead and function there until this crisis of war was over. Harry told John that he would get Kate relocated to the Hardenbergh homestead, but he was going to war with him. John immediately broke into a rage, exclaiming that he did not invite Harry to America to have him get killed in a war! Harry retorted that he did not come to America to abandon his new brother when it came time to fight!

They argued and raged for over an hour, then Harry said, "Besides, who's going to tell you where and when the enemy is coming in the bush?" Both men looked at each other with extended clarity and then broke into a gut-wrenching laugh. It was clear to John that Harry would be traveling with him to Kingston.

8

JOHN and HARRY

The journey to Kingston was a period of sharing about what was ahead for them. John informed Harry that neither the Committee of Safety for Ulster County nor the soon-to-be-formed 2nd Militia of New York allowed Negroes to enlist and serve. John was sure this would change as the conflict continued and the need for manpower increased, but for right now, Harry would not be able to enlist. Harry could not see how this made any sense, but many things these colonial white people did made no sense or had no relevancy. Harry had made up his mind that he was going to fight even if he had to be an "one-man army." John would not be taking this war on by himself. John told Harry that the only way they could end up staying together and fighting together was to play the "Slave Game."

John had already explained to Harry and Kate that, because of ignorance, fear, and outright stupidity, many white settlers had problems with the concept of a "Free Negro." They assumed all Negroes were slaves, and it made it easier for them to explain away the inferiority of an entire race of people they called Negro. John further elaborated that it would be like beating a dead horse to explain to them a "Free Black Indentured Servant." "They should get the message as you introduce yourself as Harry Freeman and Kate Freeman. Slaves are property and don't have last names; only free people have last names. So, when beneficial to what we are trying to accomplish, I suggest we allow folks to think in a manner that brings their ignorance comfort, they need to leave us alone. You and Kate will pretend, when necessary, to be slaves, the 'Slave Game.'"

Harry and Kate never cared what other people thought of them, but they did see the benefit of reducing tension, conflict, and obstacles from ignorant people both White and Black. The "Slave Game" was fine with them because they trusted their brother John L Hardenbergh. If really pushed on the matter, they had no problem letting you know who HARRY FREEMAN and KATE FREEMAN really were! So, Lt. John L Hardenbergh proceeded to Kingston, NY with his slave Harry Freeman.

Arriving in Kingston, Col. Graham informed Hardenbergh of the situation and their urgent need for information about the enemy. He told John that they were terribly outnumbered by the British and that the only way they could defeat them was to have scouting information in order to stay ahead of them. John assured him that he and a small detachment could be the eyes and ears for the army in the midst of this great Wilderness.

Once settled in their tent John told Harry, "They want us to be the eyes and ears of the army in the Bush." Harry laughed and told John, "With our hearing like an owl's and our vision like an eagle's, we surely will win this war!"

Lt. Hardenbergh of the 2nd New York Continental Regiment didn't have to wait long. John with his detachment, which included Harry Freeman, had identified Gen. Howe's movement. Such timely information would allow Gen. Washington to escape out of New York at White Plains with the Continental Army. Not only did John and Harry and the other members of the platoon reconnoiter the battle at White Plains, they fought bravely as part of the 2nd New York Continental Regiment.

As the war continued, Lt. John Hardenbergh was ordered to the supply depot at Peekskill. Staying true to their reconnaissance role, they discovered a flotilla of British ships in Peekskill Bay. This keen scouting made it possible for Gen. McDougall to retreat to Gallows Hill, saving as much provisions as his undermanned unit could escape with.

Harry and John continued to work in tandem, even though Harry was technically a slave and would never receive any notice, recognition, or benefits for his service. John knew what he was doing and would be eternally grateful for the love and commitment his African brother was giving. Harry was the first scout to report that the British had ended their siege on Fort Stanwix which allowed Col. VanCourtlandt, to whom John was attached, to proceed to join Gen. Poor and proceed to the first battle of Stillwater under Gen. Benedict Arnold, where Gen. Burgoyne surrendered.

Through the winter at Valley Forge, the battle at Monmouth, the stationing at Fort Penn, the fighting near Morristown, to the defending of West Point to the capturing, guarding, and execution of Major Andre near Tappan, to protecting the western frontier of Ulster county, John and Harry were together. Later in the war, John was promoted to Captain of Levies, General Washington's special forces for reconnaissance and special assignment.

They culminated their Revolutionary War experience in the frontiers of Ulster County when a large force of Butler's Rangers and Indians were near Warwasing, planning to massacre the settlers in the vicinity. Captain Hardenbergh, Harry, and nine men thwarted their attempts.

While they were not at Yorktown to witness General Cornwallis's surrender to General Washington and General Conte de Rochambeau, head of the French Army, the war was over.

John and Harry returned home. John to a hero's homecoming and Harry to an afterthought moment as his perceived "slave." Captain John L Hardenbergh would not allow such disrespect. Harry rode at his side through Rosendale Village, while Harry smiled and gleefully waved, absorbing the warm welcome of respect for their sacrifice to the new nation.

They settled back into their home lives and renewed their visions in Ulster County; until John was contacted by Moses Dewitt, the brother of Simeon Dewitt, the surveyor general of New York State.

The New York State Legislature had abolished the Indian titles to most of their lands in the State. Now they were going to give these lands to the soldiers who had fought in the war. The track of land encompassed 1.7 million acres and needed to be surveyed (this tract of land would include today's counties of Onondaga, Cayuga, Seneca, Cortland, Tompkins, Oswego, and Wayne). Soldiers from non-commissioned ranks down would receive one lot. Officers would receive larger shares according to rank. Simeon Dewitt wanted Col. John L Hardenbergh, along with Moses Dewitt, to survey this land and prepare an accounting for distribution.

John accepted the position of adventure. So, he and Harry had one more task before they could get back to their visions and work in Ulster County.

John and Harry undertook this challenge with great diligence and accuracy. The area that John and Harry was surveying took them to the northern New York area called the Finger Lakes Region. A stretch of five lakes created by glaciers, with rolling hills and resources abundantly plentiful for the development of a great economy for a great community, caught John's eye. He began thinking how this location would be perfect for his plans, but the problem was the commitment he had made to the territory he was developing in Ulster County.

John shared with Harry his dilemma of desire. Harry listened patiently to John's pros about this certain piece of land in the Onondaga area. John continued to muse about all the work that they had done in Ulster County and to feel guilty about abandoning the years of work.

Harry expressed his support for John and told him that God was the only one who could bring him the clarity that he needed. Harry continued to assure him that whatever his decision, he and Kate would support him completely. Harry told him if he decided to purchase the new property, Kate and he would move to the new land in the Finger Lakes and start clearing the land and build a few buildings while he finalized his business in Ulster County.

John thanked Harry for his advice and proceeded to separate himself from everybody and commune with God. It became clear to John that God had much more work that needed to be done, and John was to do it in the Finger Lakes Region of the state. Following this course would take him almost two hundred miles from what had been home all his life, but if that's where God wanted him to go, then it would be done. John did what was necessary to purchase the land.

Harry and Kate Freeman started the long trek to the new territory that John had just purchased near Owasco Lake. The Freemans took two wagons and the necessary supplies to clear land and build structures. It took them nearly two weeks to arrive in the area designated for development. It wasn't long before they had cleared a parcel of land and built several bark shelters, which became known as Hardenbergh's Corners. John handed his Ulster County operations over to several cousins, then he joined Harry and Kate at their new homestead. John and Harry talked about the proper placement of a gristmill and sawmill and other developments. They were big on attracting more people to the area and creating more marketable business opportunity because of the Owasco Outlet's great energy potential.

John had to return to Rosendale to transact some final business related to his appointment by Governor George Clinton as one of three commissioners to lay out and construct the Genesee Turnpike. The Genesee Turnpike would be the major east to west thoroughfare through the Finger Lakes Region.

While in Rosendale Village, John met Mary Bevier at a local social gathering. John was totally smitten by Mary's charm and spirit. It wasn't long before he and Mary Bevier were betrothed and married. Unfortunately, Mary would die before being able to join him at Hardenbergh's Corners in the Finger Lakes. John was happy to be completed with the inclusion of Mary, but now he had to learn how to address the hurt and grief from losing Mary. His only solace was his faith, and Harry, who shared how God brought him through the abuse of Kate and the loss of Chipo. He had been looking forward to introducing her to Harry and Kate and sharing their visions together.

Hardenbergh's Corners was booming. Settlers were arriving daily, and the community was prospering. Harry had identified tracts of lands that he desired to purchase from John. They worked out the arrangements to extend their length of indentured servitude to cover the purchase of those parcels of land.

Harry and Kate had particular designs on the section of land located on the upper part of the Owasco Outlet. They would create a "Free Slave Colony" called New Guinea. New Guinea would serve two major purposes. First, it would provide a safe haven for newly emancipated slaves, as New York and other Northern states were inching closer to abolishing slavery. Second, it would become an ongoing "Employment Service" for the businesses along the Owasco Outlet and the community in general. New Guinea would be fourteen acres on the Upper Owasco Outlet of freedom, income, and security for Africans starting a new life in a new land.

Hardenbergh's Corners was becoming the community that John and Harry had envisioned, and now love was blooming again in John's life. Martina Brinkerhoff had moved to the area with her father, Deacon Roeliff Brinkerhoff, and fell in love with the co-founder of Hardenbergh's Corners, John L Hardenbergh. Love flourished on both sides of the equation as John fell "head over heels" for Martina.

Their wedding was a major event for the growing hamlet of Hardenbergh's Corners. The wedding was held at the Reformed Protestant Dutch Church. John wanted to include Harry and Kate in the formal wedding proceedings, but Harry said to him, "My brother, we know you love us and want to share this happy occasion, but remember, too many of these people only see color. Once again it would be better to give them the illusion that they are comfortable with instead of having racist opposition to our efforts."

Harry and Kate, along with John and Martina, settled into being parents while building their businesses and their respective communities. Harry's employment service business was booming, and John had mills and interests in other businesses that were making him a very rich man.

It was getting more and more difficult for Harry and John to get away for time in the "Bush." The Wilderness was where they could freely commune and enjoy God's nature. One of their true joys was visiting their old friend, Captain Sunfish.

They had first met Captain Sunfish during the Sullivan Campaign in the war. Captain Sunfish was a huge, strapping "Son of Africa." He was of the Kombe Clan of the Bantu Tribe; he was a bodyguard (mlinzi) to the Kombe Chieftain Sithembile (See-them-bill-lay). Capt. Sunfish's name was Onyeka (Nay-ka). Onyeka stood six feet, seven inches tall and weighed 260 pounds of muscle and determination. His lore and legend on the battlefield and concerning safeguarding Chief Sithembile of the Kombe Clan was well established at an early age.

Onyeka was attending a relative's wedding among the Lengi Clan when the attack of the Clear People in the middle of the night took him captive. Onyeka was sold into slavery in what was Kentucky County, Virginia, which would become the state of Kentucky. His stay on that plantation was very short. In a violent escape where Sunfish killed one of the plantation's overseers, three slave catchers and their dogs that were in pursuit of him; he crossed the Ohio River and ventured to the western wilderness of the state of New York. Capt. Sunfish settled among the Seneca Nation and had moved close to the Genesee River, where he took a Seneca Nation bride.

Sunfish fought and clawed his way to dominance that maneuvered him into commanding and controlling the Indian Village of Kanaghsaws. After the war, more "Sons of Africa" began moving into the western wilderness of New York State. Harry had reacquainted himself with Capt. Sunfish and came across an old Revolutionary War comrade Prince Taylor.

Prince Taylor served with the 1st Rhode Island Regiment, better known as the "Black Battalion." Prince was not from Rhode Island, but when given a chance to fight, fight he did! He was at Yorktown for the surrender of Gen. Cornwallis and concluded his service to his country in the Hudson Valley of New York State.

Harry, John, and Prince all served together briefly during the Revolutionary War but had developed an inseparable bound. When Harry returned home from his wilderness venture, he immediately informed John about his reunion with Prince Taylor and Capt. Sunfish. John was elated! He told Harry to prepare for one of their "Bush Outings." John and Harry's "Bush Outings" meant that they would leave the settlement of Hardenbergh's Corners and spend seven to ten days in the deep wilderness of Western New York. The "Bush" was where they would laugh and hunt in the solitude of "God's Country" and just enjoy each other's company without the politics and cares of society.

As Hardenbergh's Corners was growing, John was becoming less enthralled with the idea of people living so close together. It was now considered a village with laws and regulations necessary to allow a large community of people to reside in peace and harmony. He was also becoming weary of such a fast-growing community bringing undo attention to him and his family by carrying his name. It was never his intention to create anything that remotely resembled the hustle and bustle of New York City.

John thought he was becoming a participant in destroying a "Way of Life" he cherished. He had lost himself in a poem, "The Deserted Village" by Oliver Goldsmith, and found solace in what was happening and what he must do as the leading member of the community. He and Harry had been so busy running enterprises that he had not had the opportunity to share with his brother his agonizing concerns about what Hardenbergh's Corners was becoming. This "Bush Outing" would give him the opportunity to share his feelings with Harry. Harry sent word to Prince Taylor, Captain Sunfish, and the other "Sons of Africa" that he and John was coming for a stopover.

Harry and John were going west of the Genesee River to meet with their old friends. The three-day journey allowed them to unwind and share their feelings and concerns without inhibitions. Harry shared his concern that many of the new white settlers to the village where new immigrants that were truly "MEAN" to the black settlers in the village. Clawing for everything they wanted to achieve, they used the color of their skin as the prime criteria to be allowed to achieve in Hardenbergh's Corners. They lamented about how it was so easy for people to disrespect and misuse a fellow human being. They realized that it was based on a lack of a "spiritual foundation" and that God could only change this misguided approach to life. What would be required from them would be prayer, patience, and tolerance, whether John and Harry liked it or not.

John told Harry that his vision of a community, like Rosendale Village, was turning into a nightmare. As far as John was concerned, Hardenbergh's Corners was turning into everything that John did not want his name attached to. He told Harry about Oliver Goldsmith's poem "The Deserted Village." On hearing the name of the poem Harry shook his head and expressed his concerns about the acceptance of anything related to a "Deserted Village." John chuckled and explained that it was a "heroic couplet" that was extremely long. He was contemplating suggesting that village change its name to "Auburn," which appears in the first line and doesn't connote the real meaning of loss and despair of the entire poem. John recited the first line of the poem, "Sweet Auburn, the loveliest village of the plain." Harry rubbed his chin and exclaimed, "That will work."

John, Harry, Captain Sunfish, Prince Taylor, Joseph "Black Joe" Hodge, Ebeneezer "Indian" Allan, and Asa Dunbar sat around the fire smoking, drinking Black Joe's apple cider, laughing, reminiscing, catching up on each other's lives and families. They only got serious when discussing current affairs.

First, was the Fugitive Slave Law of 1793. While it had been law for several years now, it spoke of some bizarre formula for the freedom of some slaves. Its real purpose was strengthening the ability to catch runaway slaves with the assistance of local and state officials. There had been a major influx of slave catchers roaming in Upstate New York creating concern for those blacks without papers. Asa and Capt. Sunfish made it clear that Lake Ontario and the Genesee River would run red with blood before they would return to slavery, and if local officials attempt to intercede in behalf of slave catchers, then so be it. Harry and John told them that there weren't any additional activities from slave catchers in the Hardenbergh's Corners' area. Then Harry stated with a firm resolved, "It wouldn't be too healthy for them to be snooping around New Guinea."

Second was that more white settlers were moving into the Western Wilderness. Black Joe had a brisk trade with a lot of these new settlers at his trading post. Indian Allan, who was Captain Sunfish's son-in-law, had been approached by a Col. Rochester about selling him about a hundred acres. Indian was thinking it was getting too crowded, and it might be time to pull up stakes. Prince Taylor sipped his cider and told the gathering how his tranquility was broken by a visit of two important white men, James Madison and Thomas Jefferson. "What in the world would cause two chief white men to visit the Wilderness? It can't be good for me! Besides, they were surprised that I had white indentured servants," bemoaned Taylor.

Everyone around the campfire jumped in amazement, Jefferson and Madison, here? Something was up, and the one thing they were assured of was that life was going to be changing for all of them. Asa Dunbar was extremely nervous about all these current events and was seriously thinking about giving up his salt business, selling his land, and moving to Canada. Harry spent the rest of the night trying to convince Asa to rethink his position. Harry wanted Asa to go into partnership and business with him transporting and selling salt in the Hardenbergh's Corners' area. Asa was not budging. He told Harry, "Harry, you are a free man, and John would support and protect your freedom at any cost. I'm a runaway. I get caught, it's back to a plantation. What would happen to my family? They'll get taken, too!"

Harry told him he understood, and Sunfish said that this was not how they should spend their last night together on what somebody else is going to do! They all laughed and got back to eating, drinking, and telling stories.

Early the next morning Harry and John rose and parted company with the others. As they tracked closer to Hardenbergh's Corners, they realized that their lives were changing forever, and so was the vision of their unobtrusive hamlet of Hardenbergh's Corner. This prompted John and Harry to look deep into each other's eyes and erupt into an earthquake of laughter. All they would say for the remainder of the journey home was, "Sweet Auburn, loveliest village of the plain... Sweet Auburn, the loveliest village of the plain... Sweet Auburn, loveliest village of the plain...", with intermittent laughter interspersed. John said, "AUBURN will be our new name."

8 $\frac{1}{2}$

THE DESERTED VILLAGE (1770)
by OLIVER GOLDSMITH
(FYI, Optional Information)

Sweet Auburn, loveliest village of the plain,
Where health and plenty cheered the laboring swain,
Where smiling spring its earliest visit paid,
And parting summer's lingering blooms delayed,
Dear lovely bowers of innocence and ease,
Seats of my youth, when every sport could please,
How often have I loitered o'er thy green,
Where humble happiness endeared each scene!
How often have I paused on every charm,
The sheltered cot, the cultivated farm,
The never-failing brook, the busy mill,
The decent church that topt the neighbouring hill,
The hawthorn bush, with seats beneath the shade,
For talking age and whispering lovers made!
How often have I blest the coming day,
When toil remitting lent its turn to play,

And all the village train, from labour free,
Led up their sports beneath the spreading tree,
While many a pastime circled in the shade,
The young contending as the old surveyed;
And many a gambol frolicked o'er the ground,
And slights of art and fears of strength went round;
And still as each repeated pleasure tired,
Succeeding sports the mirthful band inspired;
The dancing pair that simply sought renown
By holding out to tire each other down;
The swain mistrustless of his smutted face,
While secret laughter tittered round the place;
The bashful virgin's side-long looks of love,
The matron's glance that would those looks reprove!
These were thy charms, sweet village; sports like these,
With sweet succession, taught even toil to please;
These round thy bowers their cheerful influence shed,
These were thy charms—But all these charms are fled.
Sweet smiling village, loveliest of the lawn,
Thy sports are fled, and all thy charms withdrawn;
Amidst thy bowers the tyrant's hand is seen,
And desolation saddens all thy green:
One only master grasps the whole domain,
And half a tillage stints thy smiling plain;
No more thy glassy brook reflects the day,
But, choaked with sedges, works its weedy way;
Along thy glades, a solitary guest,
The hollow-sounding bittern guards its nest:
Amidst thy desert walks the lapwing flies,
And tires their echoes with unvaried cries.

Sunk are thy bowers, in shapeless ruin all,
And the long grass o'ertops the mouldering wall;
And trembling, shrinking from the spoiler's hand,
Far, far away, thy children leave the land.
Ill fares the land, to hastening ills a prey,
Where wealth accumulates, and men decay:
Princes and lords may flourish, or may fade;
A breath can make them, as a breath has made;
But a bold peasantry, their country's pride,
When once destroyed, can never be supplied.
A time there was, ere England's griefs began,
When every rood of ground maintained its man;
For him light labour spread her wholesome store,
Just gave what life required, but gave no more:
His best companions, innocence and health;
And his best riches, ignorance of wealth.
But times are altered; trade's unfeeling train
Usurp the land and dispossess the swain;
Along the lawn, where scattered hamlets rose,
Unwieldy wealth and cumbrous pomp repose;
And every want to opulence allied,
And every pang that folly pays to pride.
Those gentle hours that plenty bade to bloom,
Those calm desires that asked but little room,
Those healthful sports that graced the peaceful scene,
Lived in each look, and brightened all the green;
These, far departing seek a kinder shore,
And rural mirth and manners are no more.
Sweet Auburn! Parent of the blissful hour,
Thy glades forlorn confess the tyrant's power.

Here as I take my solitary rounds,
Amidst thy tangling walks, and ruined grounds,
And, many years elapsed, return to view
Where once the cottage stood, the hawthorn grew,
Remembrance wakes with all her busy train,
Swells at my breast, and turns the past to pain.
In all my wanderings round this world of care,
In all my griefs—and God has given my share—
I still had hopes, my latest hours to crown,
Amidst these humble bowers to lay me down;
To husband out life's taper at the close,
And keep the flame from wasting by repose.
I still had hopes, for pride attends us still,
Amidst the swains to shew my book-learned skill,
Around my fire an evening groupe to draw,
And tell of all I felt, and all I saw;
And, as an hare whom hounds and horns pursue,
Pants to the place from whence at first she flew,
I still had hopes, my long vexations past,
Here to return—and die at home at last.
O blest retirement, friend of life's decline,
Retreats from care that never must be mine,
How happy he who crowns, in shades like these
A youth of labour with an age of ease;
Who quits a world where strong temptations try,
And since 'tis hard to combat, learns to fly!
For him no wretches, born to work and weep,
Explore the mine, or tempt the dangerous deep;
No surly porter stands in guilty state
To spurn imploring famine from the gate,

But on he moves to meet his latter end,
Angels around befriending virtue's friend;
Bends to the grave with unperceived decay,
While resignation gently slopes the way;
And, all his prospects brightening to the last,
His Heaven commences ere the world be past!
Sweet was the sound, when oft at evening's close,
Up yonder hill the village murmur rose;
There, as I past with careless steps and slow,
The mingling notes came soften'd from below;
The swain responsive as the milk-maid sung,
The sober herd that lowed to meet their young,
The noisy geese that gabbed o'er the pool,
The playful children just let loose from school,
The watch-dog's voice that bayed the whispering wind,
And the loud laugh that spoke the vacant mind,
These all in sweet confusion sought the shade,
And filled each pause the nightingale had made.
But now the sounds of population fail,
No cheerful murmurs fluctuate in the gale,
No busy steps the grass-grown foot-way tread,
For all the bloomy flush of life is fled.
All but yon widowed, solitary thing
That feebly bends beside the plashy spring;
She, wretched matron, forced in age, for bread,
To strip the brook with mantling cresses spread,
To pick her wintry faggot** from the thorn,
(**Author's Clarity—In the 18th and19th centuries, the
word "faggot" meant: "A bundle of sticks" or "a meat-
ball of pluck (entrails etc.) and offal (minced parts)."

Its derogatory connotation that we are familiar with
today was not used until the 20th century, circa 1913.
Clearly Goldsmith was expressing "A Bundle of Sticks"
in the Deserted Village.}
To seek her nightly shed, and weep till morn;
She only left of all the harmless train,
The sad historian of the pensive plain.
Near yonder copse, where once the garden smiled,
And still where many a garden-flower grows wild;
There, where a few torn shrubs the place disclose,
The village preacher's modest mansion rose.
A man he was, to all the country dear,
And passing rich with forty pounds a year;
Remote from towns he ran his godly race,
Nor e'er had changed, nor wish to change his place;
Unpractised he to fawn, or seek for power,
By doctrines fashioned to the varying hour;
Far other aims his heart had learned to prize,
More skilled to raise the wretched than to rise.
His house was known to all the vagrant train,
He child their wanderings but relieved their pain;
The long-remembered beggar was his guest,
Whose beard descending swept his aged breast;
The ruined spendthrift, now no longer proud,
Claim'd kindred there, and had his claims allowed;
The broken soldier, kindly bade to stay,
State by his fire, and talked the night away;
Wept o'er his wounds, or, tales of sorrow done,
Shouldered his crutch, and shewd how fields were
won.

Pleased with his guest, the good man learned to glow,
And quite forgot their vices in their woe;
Carless their merits, or their faults to scan,
His pity gave ere charity began.
Thus to relieve the wretched was his pride,
And even his failings leaned to Virtue's side;
But in his duty prompt at every call,
He watched and wept, he prayed and felt, for all.
And, as a bird each fond endearment tries,
To tempt its new-fledged offspring to the skies;
He tried each art, reproved each dull delay,
Allured to brighter worlds, and led the way.
Beside the bed where parting life was layed,
And sorrow, guilt, and pain, by turns, dismayed
The reverend champion stood. At his control
Despair and anguish fled the struggling soul;
Comfort came down the trembling wretch to raise,
And his last faltering accents whispered praise.
At church, with meek and unaffected grace,
 His looks adorned the venerable place;
Truth from his lips prevailed with double sway,
And fools, who came to scoff, remained to pray.
The service past, around the pious man,
With steady zeal, each honest rustic man,
Even children followed, with endearing wile,
And plucked his gown, to share the good man's smile.
His ready smile a parent's warmth exprest,
Their welfare pleased him, and their cares distrest:
To them his heart, his love, his griefs were given,
But all his serious thoughts had rest in Heaven.

As some tall cliff that lifts its awful form,
Swells from the vale, and midway leaves the storm,
Tho' round its breast the rolling clouds are spread,
Eternal sunshine settles on its head.
Beside yon straggling fence that skirts the way,
With blossomed furze unprofitably gay,
There, in his noisy mansion, skill'd to rule,
The village master taught his little school;
A man severe he was, and stern to view,
I knew him well, and every truant knew;
Well had the boding tremblers learned to trace
The day's disasters in his morning face;
Full well they laughed, with counterfeited glee,
At all his jokes, for many a joke had he:
Full well the busy whisper circling round,
Conveyed the dismal tidings when he frowned;
Yet he was kind, or if severe in aught,
The love he bore to learning was in fault;
The village all declared how much he knew;
'Twas certain he could write, and cypher too;
Lands he could measure, terms and tides presage,
And ev'n the story ran that he could gauge.
In arguing too, the parson owned his skill,
For even tho' vanquished, he could argue still;
While words of learned length and thundering sound,
Amazed the gazing rustics ranged around;
And still they gazed, and still the wonder grew,
That one small head could carry all he knew.
But past is all his fame. The very spot
Where many a time he triumphed, is forgot.

Near yonder thorn, that lifts its head on high,
Where once the sign-post caught the passing eye,
Low lies that house where nut-brown draughts inspired,
Where grey-beard mirth and smiling toil retired,
Where village statesmen talked with looks profound,
And news much older than their ale went round.
Imagination fondly stoops to trace
The parlour splendours of that festive place;
The white-washed wall, the nicely sanded floor,
The varnished clock that clicked behind the door;
The chest contrived a double debt to pay,
A bed by night, a chest of drawers by day;
The pictures placed for ornament and use,
The twelve good rules, the royal game of goose;
The hearth, except when winter chill'd the day,
With aspen boughs, and flowers, and fennel gay;
While broken tea-cups, wisely kept for shew,
Ranged o'er the chimney, glistened in a row.
Vain transitory splendours! Could not all
Reprieve the tottering mansion from its fall!
Obscure it sinks, nor shall it more impart
An hour's importance to the poor man's heart;
Thither no more the peasant shall repair
To sweet oblivion of his daily care;
No more the farmer's news, the barber's tale,
No more the woodman's ballad shall prevail;
No more the smith his dusky brow shall clear,
Relax his ponderous strength, and lean to hear;
The host himself no longer shall be found
Careful to see the mantling bliss go round;

Nor the coy maid, half willing to be prest,
Shall kiss the cup to pass it to the rest.
Yes! Let the rich deride, the proud disdain,
These simple blessings of the lowly train;
To me more dear, congenial to my heart,
One native charm, than all the gloss of art;
Spontaneous joys, where Nature has its play,
The soul adopts, and owns their first-born sway;
Lightly they frolic o'er the vacant mind,
Unenvied, unmolested, unconfined.
But the long pomp, the midnight masquerade,
With all the freaks of wanton wealth arrayed,
In these, ere triflers half their wish obtain,
The toiling pleasure sickens into pain;
And, even while fashion's brightest arts decoy,
The heart distrusting asks, if this be joy.
Ye friends to truth, ye statesmen who survey
The rich man's joys increase, the poor's decay,
'Tis yours to judge, how wide the limits stand
Between a splendid and a happy land.
Proud swells the tide with loads of freighted ore,
And shouting Folly hails them from her shore;
Hoards even beyond the miser's wish abound,
And rich men flock from all the world around.
Yet count our gains. This wealth is but a name
That leaves our useful products still the same.
Not so the loss. The man of wealth and pride
Takes up a space that many poor supplied;
Space for his lake, his park's extended bounds,
Space for his horses, equipage, and hounds:

The robe that wraps his limbs in silken sloth,
Has robbed the neighbouring fields of half their growth:
His seat, where solitary sports are seen,
Indignant spurns the cottage from the green:
Around the world each needful product flies,
For all the luxuries the world supplies.
While thus the land adorned for pleasure, all
In barren splendor feebly waits the fall.
As some fair female unadorned and plain,
Secure to please while youth confirms her reign,
Slights every borrowed charm that dress supplies,
Nor shares with art the triumph of her eyes.
But when those charms are past, for charms are frail,
When time advances, and when lovers fail,
She then shines forth, solicitous to bless,
In all the glaring impotence of dress.
Thus fares the land, by luxury betrayed:
In nature's simplest charms at first arrayed;
But verging to decline, its spendours rise,
Its vistas strike, its palaces surprize;
While, scourged by famine from the smiling land,
The mournful peasant leads his humble band;
And while he sinks, without one arm to save,
The country blooms—a garden, and a grave.
Where then, ah where, shall poverty reside,
To scape the pressure of contiguous pride?
If to some common's fenceless limits strayed,
He drives his flock to pick the scanty blade,
Those fenceless fields the sons of wealth divide,
And ev'n the bare-worn common is denied.

If to the city sped—What waits him there?
To see profusion that he must not share;
To see ten thousand baneful arts combined
To pamper luxury, and thin mankind;
To see those joys the sons of pleasure know,
Extorted from this fellow-creature's woe.
Here while the courtier glitters in brocade,
There the pale artist plies the sickly trade;
Here while the proud their long-drawn pomps display,
There the black gibber glooms beside the way.
The dome where Pleasure holds her midnight reign,
Here, richly deckt, admits the gorgeous train;
Tumultuous grandeur crowds the blazing square,
The rattling chariots clash, the torches glare.
Sure scenes like these no troubles e'er annoy!
Sure these denote one universal joy!
Are these thy serious thoughts?—Ah, turn thine eyes
Where the poor houseless shivering female lies.
She once, perhaps, in village plenty blest,
Has wept at tales of innocence distrest;
Her modest looks the cottage might adorn
Sweet as the primrose peeps beneath the thorn:
Now lost to all; her friends, her virtue fled,
Near her betrayer's door she lays her head,
And, pinch'd with cold, and shrinking from the shower,
With heavy heart deplores that luckless hour
When idly first, ambitious of the town,
She left her wheel and robes of country brown.
Do thine, sweet Auburn, thine, the loveliest train,
Do thy fair tribes participate her pain?

Even now, perhaps, by cold and hunger led,
At proud men's door they ask a little bread!
Ah, no. To distant climes, a dreary scene,
Where half the convex world intrudes between,
Through torrid tracts with fainting steps they go,
Where wild Altama murmurs to their woe.
Far different there from all that charm'd before,
The various terrors of that horrid shore;
Those blazing suns that dart a downward ray,
And fiercely shed intolerable day;
Those matted woods where birds forget to sing,
But silent bats in drowsy clusters cling;
Those poisonous fields with rank luxuriance crowned,
Where the dark scorpion gathers death around;
Where at each step the stranger fears to wake
The rattling terrors of the vengeful snake;
Where crouching tigers wait their hapless prey,
And savage men, more murderous still than they;
While oft in whirls the mad tornado flies,
Mingling the ravaged landscape with the skies.
Far different these from every former scene,
The cooling brook, the grassy vested green,
The breezy covert of the warbling grove,
That only shelter'd thefts of harmless love.
Good Heaven! What sorrows gloom'd that parting day,
That called them from their native walks away;
When the poor exiles, every pleasure past,
Hung round their bowers, and fondly looked their last,
And took a long farewell, and wished in vain
For seats like these beyond the western main;

And shuddering still to face the distant deep,
Returned and wept, and still returned to weep.
The good old sire the first prepared to go
To new found worlds, and wept for others woe.
But for himself, in conscious virtue brave,
He only wished for worlds beyond the grave.
His lovely daughter, lovelier in her tears,
The fond companion of his helpless years,
Silent went next, neglectful of her charms,
And left a lover's for a father's arms.
With louder plaints the mother spoke her woes,
And blessed the cot where every pleasure rose;
And kist her thoughtless babes with many a tear,
And claspt them close, in sorrow doubly dear;
In all the silent manliness of grief.
O luxury! Thou curst by Heaven's decree,
How ill exchanged are things like these for thee!
How do thy potions, with insidious joy,
Diffuse their pleasures only to destroy!
Kingdoms, by thee, to sickly greatness grown,
Boast of a florid vigour not their own;
At every draught more large and large they grow,
A bloated mass of rank unwieldy woe;
Till sapped their strength, and every part unsound,
Down, down they sink, and spread a ruin round.
Even now the devastation is begun,
And half the business of destruction done;
Even now, methinks, as pondering here I stand,
I see the rural virtues leave the land:
Down where yon anchoring vessel spreads the sail,
That idly waiting flaps with every gale,

Downward they move, a melancholy band,
Pass from the shore, and darken all the strand.
Contented toil, and hospitable care,
And kind connubial tenderness, are there;
And piety with wishes placed above,
And steady loyalty, and faithful love.
And thou, sweet Poetry, thou loveliest maid,
Still first to fly where sensual joys invade;
Unfit in these degenerate times of shame,
To catch the heart, or strike for honest fame;
Dear charming nymph, neglected and decried,
My shame in crowds, my solitary pride;
Thou source of all my bliss, and all my woe,
That found'st me poor at first, and keep'st me so;
Thou guide by which the nobler arts excel,
Thou nurse of every virtue, fare thee well!
Farewell, and O where'er thy voice be tried,
On Torno's cliff, on Pambamarca's side,
Whether were equinoctial fervours glow,
Or winter wraps the polar world in snow,
Still let thy voice, prevailing over time,
Redress the rigours of the inclement clime;
Aid slighted truth with thy persuasive strain,
Teach erring man to spurn the rage of gain;
Teach him, that states of native strength possest,
Tho' very poor, may still be very blest;
That trade's proud empire hastes to swift decay,
As ocean sweeps the labour'd mole away;
While self-dependent power can time defy,
As rocks resist the billows and the sky.

9

FOUNDATIONS ANEW

John Hardenbergh and Harry Freeman returned from their "Bush Outing" resolved to work on changing the name of the village to Auburn. John knew that it was going to take some time and that he would have to develop a ground swell of interest in name change. Hardenbergh's Corners was rapidly evolving. The Genesee Pike was moving along in its development and conclusion. The Pike was creating a great deal of prosperity, development, political shenanigans, and vile racial discrimination. Both the Freemans and the Hardenberghs had contributed to the population boom in Hardenbergh's Corners.

Martina and John had brought into the community two children, Maria Hardenbergh and John Herring Hardenbergh. Not to be left out of the population explosion, Kate and Harry brought into the community seven children, Caroline Freeman, Harry Freeman Jr, James Freeman, Sidney Freeman, Jane Freeman, Morgan Lewis "Luke" Freeman, and Platt Roundtree "P.R." Freeman.

Harry and John where now entrepreneurs and fathers. John's mills and his other business ventures were assuring the security for his family. His "Golden Goose" was being a part of developing the Genesee Pike. The Genesee Pike at its conclusion would stretch from Utica to Canandaigua, a total of 117 miles. John had a financial interest in the waystations along the Pike due to his partnership with Levi Stevens. He also had considerable holdings in the hotel in Auburn.

Levi Stevens had secured an "exclusive right" addressing the construction and operation of the Genesee Pike. Hardenbergh and Stevens had a working relation; John was able to provide stone from the different quarries that were springing up in the northern area of Hardenbergh Corners. The Genesee Pike was being engineered to be over sixty feet wide and placed a high demand for crushed stone. John was able to allow Harry and Kate to share in this bonanza by supplying laborers, hauling supplies, and providing additional services from Elbridge to Geneva.

During its construction, Kate would prepare and sell a hearty stew with fried cakes at the work camps along the route, particularly during the cold months, October to June. She would provide workers a place to wash their clothes and provide sanitation services for the work camps.

Meanwhile, the Freeman Family was expanding its "Employment Service." Free African Americans and runaway slaves were flocking to New Guinea. Some were highly skilled, and some were just basic laborers. Harry Freeman's "New Guinea Employment Service" was prepared to meet the needs of any employer along the Owasco Outlet or in the vicinity of Auburn.

Yes, Auburn! The village council had voted to change the name of Hardenbergh's Corners, New York to Auburn, New York. Harry and John were elated about the name change and celebrated in their traditional way, together.

John and Harry were getting older and had lost the rambunctiousness of their youth, but they still enjoyed spending time together. John had built a big house right on the southern boundary of the village on South St., and Harry had properties on Fort St. and Cornell St., south of the village; he chose to reside at New Guinea. The two old friends lived less than a half a mile from each other, which was a short walk down the hill for Harry. Harry told Kate that the walk up the hill was what keeping him spry and feeling half his age. Kate quipped, "Then how come you come to bed smelling like horse liniment after those trips?"

Harry was beginning to get worried about John. Even though John was trying to be his old stoic self, Harry could see that this organized corporate "mean-fest" called a village was making his brother weary. John did not expect what he had discovered in creating a community of diverse people with diverse intentions.

Hardenbergh had been spoiled by his existence in Rosendale Village. Rosendale had provided a haven for families of the same lineage, heritage, background, religious beliefs, and intents. A homogenous community Auburn was not. Auburn would never be a Rosendale Village. The notoriety and importance Auburn had attained could never sustain the rudimentary elements of peace that human beings required. Rosendale Village was a homogenous community and did not need tolerance or reshaping every piece of its puzzle to fit comfortably in its proper position. The newly named village of Auburn required love, tolerance, and patience, all things that required an individual to work at building within themselves first before it could be exported to their community.

Love means you don't beat someone out of their possessions to increase your wants and desire. This requires a deeper and longer walk with God in your "Spirit." Having heard the story of Uriah, David, and Bathsheba in the Bible, it is clear that God hates "Greed." But "Greed" was the motivating interest of many who were settling in Auburn. There were the land speculators and con men, but the most concerning were the settlers filing in from the Northeast and new immigrants. Their desires and fears of not achieving all their selfish dreams required them to castigate, take advantage of, and disrespect any other human being who had what they want or might provide competition to perceived importance in their lives. It was a perfect blend of hatred, ignorance, and debauchery.

Without tolerance, this was a recipe straight from the pits of hell and would assure misery and despair for the African America population. The Black children were not allowed to receive an education or to attend church properly.

The saving grace to this cauldron of despair and harmful conflict was a growing group of white people coming to reside in the village, whose status in life was not in question nor their consistency in moral behavior. They were people who believed in what the Bible taught and exhibited great concern. For some white people, exhibiting great "Patience" with ignorant white people who thought the color of their skin made them superior was difficult.

These individuals of love and peace were working to change the concept that this new nation of ours, The United States of America, which was created under God, was not a melting pot of "goo." A melting pot of undistinguishable individuals that surrendered their personal characteristics to become "goo." Their belief was that "All men and women were created equal and endowed with unalienable rights." Their analogy of this belief was, "The United States of America was a 'Tossed Salad' made of different ingredients that maintain their individual characteristics, but when brought together, created a delectable dish of delightful and beneficial flavors." These individuals worked hard at trying to mitigate the hateful racial climate in Auburn and were given a name, Abolitionists.

Harry and John's responsibilities were steadily increasing. John had commercial interests in several businesses that were consuming too much time. The creation of the Genesee Pike and cursory speculations about the development of a canal had introduced a national undertone to the community. It was getting to the point where Hardenbergh was spending less time in his beloved mills and more time in meetings. Harry had built an oasis for African Americans that provided a glimpse of freedom. Harry was providing 90 percent of the employees working along the Owasco Outlet and the general vicinity. The New Guinea community was becoming a phenomenon. Every day more people were coming to find safety, comfort, and, hopefully, "Peace."

Their conversations no longer centered on "Bush Outings" and "Adventures" but on new approaches to doing business in the community. Now, for Harry and John, it was about being a father, raising children, and praying. They spent more time praying together, sitting on those tree stumps in the back of John's estate, than they did anything else. Always asking God to keep the "old man" of sin buried in them and let the "new man" of Jesus Christ shine through them in their daily walk through life. They asked the Lord to give them the strength to "Love" more in the midst of "Hate," "Deceit," and "Greed." They would pray for hours like the brothers they were, in a tag team fashion, always finishing with one scripture.

"Therefore I, a prisoner for serving the Lord, beg you to lead a life worthy of your calling, for you have been called by God. Always be humble and gentle. Be patient with each other, making allowance for each other's faults because of your love. Make every effort to keep yourselves united in the Spirit, binding yourselves together with peace. For there is one body and one Spirit, just as you have called to one glorious hope for the future. There is one Lord, one faith, one baptism, and one God and Father, who is over all and in all and living through all." (Ephesians 4:1-6, NLT)

John told Harry that everything was going well with Maria and John Herring. They were growing well in their church lessons and general education. Harry was happy to hear the Hardenbergh children were doing so well. Harry's report wasn't as gleeful. Black children were not allowed to attend public school, and the growing racist attitude of new settlers required a pronouncement of the African American being inferior in order to buttress their own wellbeing and disregard the successes of the Blacks.

Kate and he were "homeschooling" their children and teaching them family values and history that would not allow them to accept being inferior to anybody! Black children were not allowed in neither any public education settings nor any Bible study classes. Harry told John that he and Kate had taught their children to "Keep God first in everything and don't allow anyone to treat you as an inferior human being."

John told Harry that he heard that same disgusting talk by those same ignorant white settlers. John said, "They soon learned not to make those kinds of remarks around John Hardenbergh." They both agreed that prayer was the only effective weapon that they could utilize.

Hardenbergh and Freeman, in earlier days, would sit in Hardenbergh's backyard for hours and laugh and cackle about their adventures and close calls during the war combined with a gregarious accounting of their Bush Outings but would always conclude their "Gatherings" with devotion and prayer.

As time went by, Harry's walks down the hill to John's backyard became fewer and farther in between. The tenure of "the Gatherings" was evolving. The laughter wasn't as earthshakingly loud, the cackling had turned to coughing, and their devotionals and prayers where becoming extremely specific. The brisk night air brought more discomfort than relief, causing "the Gatherings" to become shorter in length. John Hardenbergh was ill.

Kate's days were consumed with raising and educating her children. Fading were the days where this industrious frontier woman would set out in a wagon to conquer any obstacles that might arise. Whether it be angry Natives, hating Whites, or conniving Africans, Kate Freeman handled the situation with unflinching nerves in the true Agooji Warrior Spirit she was taught by her mother.

Now Kate was confronted with a major concern that her mother had never taught her about, the inclusion and socialization of her children into a "Hating Society." Kate and Harry were learning and educating their children, particularly the older ones, but unfortunately, their acceptance, tolerance, and desire to be a part of this "Hating Society" was waning. Harry Jr., James, Sidney, and Jane were in complete rebellion. Caroline was momma's protégé. She had devoted herself to be a sponge, learning everything her mother Kate offered. Platt and Luke, the youngest siblings, couldn't understand the internal family struggle of "wills" which made no sense to the wellbeing of the family in the midst of this "Hating Society." Their philosophy was to listen to Dad.

The older siblings weren't interested in hearing the stories of what Mom and Dad had been through. Their concerns centered only around themselves and what they desired and thought they deserved.

Their rebellion was weighing heavy on Harry and Kate. They were living the "good life" at their parents' expense. Harry and Kate would neither tolerate nor accept this kind of uprising within their family structure. So, slowly, they estranged themselves from their own children, allowing them to see life as it truly was without the guidance and support of their family.

Harry Jr. didn't like this new arrangement. Every time he returned home and professed his allegiance to the family and its efforts, in a matter of weeks he would return to his laissez-faire lifestyle. Harry was not accepting this kind of behavior from his oldest boy and namesake. Uncle John, the Freeman children's name of choice for John Hardenbergh, had tried to intervene several times, but this was the final straw; Harry, Jr. was out. Sidney, James, and Jane choose to seek their fortune and wellbeing away from their parents. All this tumultuous behavior in the family structure hurt Harry and Kate more than their entire ordeal with the Clear People. Engulfed in this personal nightmare with their older children did not keep them from praying for them and keeping them before the throne of God day and night.

Morgan Lewis Freeman (Luke) and Platt Roundtree Freeman (P.R.) were Harry and Kate's youngest children and the ones they kept close to their side, trying to mitigate the influence of their older siblings. Luke and P.R. were as different as night and day.

Luke was a very special child whose birth and first few months of life were uncertain and frightening to Kate, Harry, and John. Harry and John spent hours sitting on those tree stumps in the backyard praying to God to save this child's life and to heal his body.

John told Harry and Kate, "If the Lord takes Luke back before he is able to establish his existence on this earth, it should at least be recorded that he was here." Harry and Kate had opposed doing this with their older children under the pretext of "keeping those folks out of our business." Kate and Harry acquiesced after praying about having Morgan Lewis Freeman's name tied up in white folks' business. So, Uncle John was allowed to register Luke's birth at the county courthouse.

Their prayers were answered. Luke's health improved, and his personality began to captivate anyone who came into his presence.

Platt Roundtree Freeman was his father's shadow. P.R., as he was known on the New Guinea property and around the village, was the dutiful son. Platt was very reserved, cordial but not outgoing. P.R. spent his time traveling with his dad, Harry Sr., and learning every aspect of the Freeman Family Businesses. P.R. was a pragmatist. He paid attention to his mother's efforts to teach him to read, add and subtract, but his real interest was learning how to conduct business with white folks in spite of white folks' shenanigans.

Platt thought his father was a master at managing the family businesses. He saw his father with individuals that needed the Freemans' services but had no intent of conducting that business fairly or in a way keeping with their professed religious beliefs as followers of Christ. He would marvel at his father's ability to mentally undress these people and beat them at their own game. Harry and Kate Freeman's businesses were thriving and contentiously under threat from greedy and hateful white folks and conniving and hating black folks.

Kate's biggest problem was instilling in her children her and Harry's values about God and how you treat and respect all people and not having it being reinforced outside of their home by the general community. People's reliance on separating the races and promoting dominance and inferiority based on skin color was countermanding their teachings to their children. The impact and result on their family was taking too large of a toil.

In spite of these attacks from the outside and inside, the Freemans kept the "Family Creed" intact:

> *"Keep God first in Everything you do; and tolerate no mess from no human being!"*

Kate and Harry had built over twenty buildings on their New Guinea property and had nearly two hundred free African Americans and runaway slaves living on their property. Business in Cayuga County was exploding. The quarries on Auburn's northside were making requests for manpower that were making it difficult to respond.

Things were changing as the village was growing. Formality and a collection of laws and legislations written and enforced at every level of life were beginning to make daily life complicated. There were many rhymes and reasons for the need of these mandates based on a growing community and services to accommodate the growth, but it was changing the lives of settlers who could not understand, keep up with, or embrace their true benefits.

Officials from the village and the county now expected the Freemans to pay them for land and property they owned. Harry was furious. "They don't cut the grass or move the snow on our property. Why should I pay them anything?" he excitedly exclaimed to Kate.

"Harry, they're building a civil community. We need a constable and schools and a library, and the roads taken care of," Kate shared calmly to her irate husband.

"Schools, library, and laws we're not allowed to share because of stupidity!" Harry shouted back.

Before another word could be uttered, Harry, Jr. burst into the house and exclaimed, "Uncle John is dead!" Silence permeated the room like a dense fog caught in the valley at daybreak. Moments transpired with everyone in the room gazing at Harry for insight and direction. Harry's response was going to be the settling elixir his family required right now with change on the horizon. It was no secret that a segment of the Auburn community thought the Freemans were "Uppity Negroes," thinking they are on an equal footing with White people.

John Hardenbergh would neither permit any bigoted conversation in his presence nor devious attempts to undermine Harry and Kate's businesses and their ownership of property. John had provided Harry advance warning about opportunities and problems. Now they were looking to their patriarch, in the middle of their loss of a family member, the comfort Uncle John's family needed and the well-being and future of the Freeman Family.

Harry rose from his seat and gathered his family close to him and said, "Let's pray." He knew what their concerns were. He knew that he did not have the answers they needed, but he knew where to get them, from God. Harry led his family in prayer. When they had finished praying for the Hardenbergh family and for direction for his family, Harry sat everyone down with whatever comforting gestures were needed.

Harry said, "Our number one concern now as a family is to help Martina, John Herring, and Maria through this very difficult time. Kate, Caroline, and Harry, you are to go down to the Hardenbergh house and assist Martina in any way you can. I'll be down momentarily to add my support. We as a family will be just fine because 'WE Keep God First in Everything' that happens to us, good or bad."

As Kate, Harry Jr., and Caroline started their trek down to the Hardenbergh's estate, Harry sent for Tootie Brown to watch the younger children. Tootie and her husband August Brown and his family were early on runaway slaves who found refuge in New Guinea. They had escaped from the eastern shore of Maryland with slave catchers trailing them. August Brown was a millwright and miller whose aptitudes and skills were extremely profitable to his owner. The eight-hundred-dollar bounty on his head and the two-hundred-dollar a piece bounty on the other four members of his family brought the Browns great notoriety in the slave catching community.

This all came to a head after the Browns had heard about a free slave colony called New Guinea in a small village called Hardenbergh's Corners, New York. It became their goal to reach this enclave not far from the Canadian border. They eventually made their way to Hardenbergh's Corners where they met Harry and Kate Freeman. Harry explained what New Guinea was about, being a safe haven for all Africans and a place for employment opportunities. Harry emphasized the fact that New Guinea was the place to be a "Free Man under God." August and Tootie were impressed with what they heard about New Guinea, as well as the fortitude of Kate and Harry. August felt comfortable in telling them where they had escaped from and who was chasing them.

August Brown was now being guided by God to do something that he had not dare do during his family's flight to freedom. He told Kate and Harry what he could do as a millwright and a miller. Harry looked at Kate, and they smiled in unison. Then Harry turned to August and said, "God has sent you here for a time like this. I'll introduce you to my brother John Hardenbergh who has just built a mill on the Owasco Outlet. There will be a great need for a millwright and someone to teach folks coming to New Guinea how to mill."

Kate then turned to Tootie and said with a wry grin, "Don't worry about slave catchers; this community is not fond of bounty hunters, and Harry and I know how to deal with them."

It seems that the Freemans had been collecting a stable of hounds and other dogs that had been trained to hunt people that Harry and Kate had retrained to hunt wilderness animals and to guard their properties. Four months after the Browns had settled into New Guinea, Hozie Cantrell with several other men showed up in the Aurelius area. Immediately, some of the New Guinea residents working in the Aurelius community informed Harry about Cantrell and his group of "paddy rollers." Harry and Kate immediately sprang into action.

Kate began by alerting her network of "Watch Women." These were members of New Guinea society who Kate had trained to be observant about anything that could impact the New Guinea community. When a specific incident or concern was identified, the network would engage immediately by securing pertinent information. "The Watch Women Network" would bring Kate anything out of the ordinary daily. When alerted about a major concern that could threaten the wellbeing of New Guinea, they would gather with Kate after the dinner hour every day until the issue was resolved.

Harry had watched the migration of every settler that had journeyed to the area. No matter how mean or racially bigoted they were, they found great comfort in not supporting "southern-style slavery." They felt like they were on the higher moral grounds, so they despised slave catchers. Slave Catchers, or Paddy Rollers, as they were known in the Black community, could find neither comfort nor support in the area. This allowed Harry and his own security element for New Guinea made up of every man and boy thirteen years and older to be an effective deterrent to the Paddy Rollers' destructive assaults.

Harry and Kate taught these male residents of New Guinea the old ways. The same that had been taught to them by their parents, and they named them the New Guinea Tree Leopards. Harry's tactics were succinct. "Surprise, Submission, and Determination" were the Tree Leopards' approach. Their "Surprise Attacks" would be when least expected and as silent as a leaf falling from a tree. "Submission" would be complete, hopefully nonviolently, but force was readily available. The extent of violence was always a determinate left up to the discretion of the Paddy Rollers.

The "Determination" to live or die was also left up to the Slave Catchers. If life was their Determination, then their choices were limited. They had to swear on a Bible to never return to the Finger Lakes Region or face immediate death. The notorious Black slave catcher Fiddler Johnson gained a hitch in his giddy-up and learned that the Finger Lakes were off limit. What they were not given a choice about was their dogs, who had not provided any warning for them; the Tree Leopards would bring female dogs to occupy the attention of the male hounds. Dogs, weapons, and anything Harry determined not necessary for their return to the South was also confiscated. Kate and Harry had become very successful at curtailing this type of bounty hunting in their area.

The Watch Women Network had secured intel that Hozie Cantrell, and four men were camped west of Hardenbergh's Corners near Half Acre road. They were heavily armed and had three dogs with them, one bloodhound and two coon hounds. They were cozy and comfortable in their camp location and were not posting night sentries.

Kate shared their discoveries with Harry, which was all the information Harry needed to resolve this threat. Harry established the time and date for the encounter with Cantrell and his compadres. The night of the attack Harry issued a "Stay in Place" order to those men of New Guinea working in the western part of the county.

They were to stay in the vicinity of the slave catchers' camp and continue to reconnoiter the situation until Harry arrived with the rest of New Guinea's Tree Leopards. Harry had some of the leopards move west on Clarke Rd. and the remainder with him moving west on the Pike Road. All were meeting at the Pike and Half Acre Road, before the 3:00 A.M. confrontation.

Hozie Cantrell and his Paddy Rollers were completely surprised and startled by the attack. Each one of them had a machete in close proximity of their throats and groins, with a pistol nudging their temples. Surprise and Submission were obtained in less than ten minutes. All that was left was Determination. It was time for Hozie and his gang to determine what would be their outcome with their encounter with the Tree Leopards. Harry sent five men back with the newly acquired weapons and dogs and began his conversation with Cantrell. In short order Hozie Cantrell was in complete agreement with all the edicts that Mr. Freeman espoused. Hozie Cantrell and his fellow slave catchers began their long trek back south. Mr. Freeman warned them that he had a network of Tree Leopards from here to the Mason-Dixie Line. Any deviation of their movement south or any attempt to wrangle a runaway slave would require the immediate termination of this agreement and would require their deaths for the violation of their agreement.

Cantrell and his cohorts began their cautious trip back south looking over their shoulders and scurrying a little faster every time they encountered an African on their journey south. Twenty years later, one of the runaway slaves named Thaddeus told Harry that if he ever made it North as far as Hardenbergh's Corners to tell Mr. Freeman that Rev. Hozie Cantrell said hello. Harry busted into laughter and said, "This is Hardenbergh's Corners, we changed our name awhile back." Harry leaning back on the wall bent over from laughing so hard, straightened a little and shared this with Thaddeus, "Son, I am Mr. Freeman. Thaddeus remembered two things. To whom much is given, much is owed, and God works in mysterious ways."

Harry took Thaddeus outside with the other new arrivals and told them the story of the Tree Leopards and Hozie Cantrell. John Hardenbergh had passed. Harry's brother, confidant, and benefactor gone to soon. One of the foundation stones, along with Harry and Kate, of this thriving community called Auburn.

Harry had not felt such despair since the death of Chipo, his daughter. Tootie was watching the younger children, and Kate and the older siblings were off to Martina's, so he walked to his quiet spot near the Outlet to gain direction from the Lord.

"Why now, Lord? Just when things were looking up and we were enjoying life and each other's company, you take my brother from me! Why, Lord? Why?" petitioned Harry.

As Harry sat there sobbing uncontrollably the Lord asked him, "I know that John coming home to Me has presented itself as an insurmountable and untimely loss to you. I raise an option to you. Either having John in your life, which has enriched the soil of your existence for a lifetime, or never having John L Hardenbergh in your life in order to avoid the emotional pain and physical loss you are experiencing now?"

Harry answered immediately. "The first one, Lord. John was the brother I never had. We were like fingers on the same hand. Definitely the first one Father!"

The Lord then said, "You have the right to grieve as long as you want. Grieving is like a 'Spiritual Toothache.' A toothache, whether spiritual or physical, will not get better by itself; it will just get worse and worse as time progresses. Eventually it will impact negatively every aspect of your spiritual, emotional, and physical being which could lead to your physical destruction and eternal spiritual death.

"Because I love you, I have sent you a remedy and cure for this 'Spiritual Toothache' known as Grief. I have sent you the teachings of my only Son the Messiah Jesus Christ. The more you adhere to the teachings of the Christ, the pain from the 'Spiritual Toothache of Grief' is reduced. If you learn to become 'Obedient' to the teachings of the Messiah, the 'Spiritual Toothache of Grief' is removed. You will then be able to dwell on the sweet memories that you have gathered about John for the rest of your life. Remember **'THE MORE JESUS, THE LESS GRIEF, THE LESS JESUS, THE MORE GRIEF.'"**

"Harry," the Lord said quietly, "remember that time heals the 'Hurt and Sting' of earthly death. Healing occurs with your spiritual growth in order to remind you and to share with the world the love John Hardenbergh and Harry Freeman shared through my Grace."

Harry sat there with the clarity that he needed to proceed through this period of Grief and Hurt. He had determined that awareness of his Obedience to the teachings of the Christ had already diminished his Grief. He decided that he would suffer through his Hurt till time provided the necessary Healing.

Harry started down the hill to join his family in bringing Martina and the children as much comfort and support as they could.

1 0

THE FUNERAL OF REMEMBERANCE

John had been made a lieutenant colonel of a regiment of militia in Onondaga County by Governor John Jay in 1796. The funeral of Lieutenant Colonel John L Hardenbergh was a resplendent pageantry of pomp and ceremony that had never been witnessed in the village of Auburn before.

Below is an accounting of John Hardenbergh's Funeral Service as recounted by Rev. Charles Hawley, D. D. in 1879. Once again "a large dose of salt" must be consumed as it pertains to Harry Freeman's relationship John Hardenbergh. **HARRY and KATE FREEMAN WERE INDENTURED SERVANTS, NOT SLAVES IN THE AMERICAS.**

The insignificance of individuals' respect and appreciation of the African American community allowed them to dedicate no time in reporting the facts related to Harry and Kate Freeman. Even to the point of excluding them as co-founders of Auburn, New York.

The posting of John's death and funeral:

"Colonel Hardenbergh died after a brief illness, on the 25th of April, 1806, in the 59th year of his age, and was buried with military honors in the North Street Cemetery. The Rev. David Higgins, the pastor of the Congregational Church of Aurelius, and the founder of the First Presbyterian Church of Auburn, preached the funeral sermon from the Epistle to the Philippians, iii (3); 20,21:

'For our conversation is in heaven; from whence also we look for the Saviour, the Lord Jesus Christ, who shall change our vile body that it may be fashioned like unto his glorious body according to the working whereby he is able even to subdue all things unto himself.'

"The horse bearing the sword and uniform of the deceased officer, was led by Harry Freeman, one of the Colonel's slaves to whom he had given his freedom. A long procession of military and citizens followed the remains to the grave. The whole scene was imposing, as a sincere tribute of the respect and esteem cherished for the man who had braved the perils of the then recent struggle for national independence, and with generous hand had laid the foundations, in the wilderness, of a well-ordered community. He had passed thirty years of his life as a soldier, a surveyor, and a pioneer settler, and had occupied the most responsible trusts in the rising settlement which owed to him its origin. He was moreover a great favorite with his fellow pioneers, and with all who were seeking new homes in the immediate vicinity, ambitious rather for the thrift of the place than for personal gains, or the promotion of selfish ends—forward and generous in all plans to establish religion, education, justice and good order, with whatever tended to the permanent prosperity and true character of the infant settlement. He was not always careful of his interests, and was sometimes imposed upon by those in whom he confided as if they were as trustworthy as himself. If a neighbor wanted a bushel or two of grain, he might be trusted to measure it himself and render his own account. In this way and in others characteristic of him, he doubtless now and then lost pecuniarily, but they gave him a strong hold upon the better and larger class of his co-pioneers, and a leading influence at this forming period in our history. Indeed, Auburn owes very much to the spirit, foresight and enterprise of its founder.

"In person, Colonel Hardenbergh was tall, of swarthy complexion, robust frame, and is said to have been a most commanding figure on horseback, in his regimentals, on military occasions. He took an active part in the politics of the day, and was decided and open in the expression of his opinions. He was a warm friend and ardent supporter of Governor George Clinton, under whom he had served in the first year of the war, and whose confidence he largely shared in the distribution of military promotions and civil appointments. A sturdy patriot, a brave soldier, a civilian, honored and trusted in public station and in private life, he has fairly won the gratitude with which communities are wont to remember their founders."

Also in keeping with the tradition of ignorance and bias towards African Americans, it was reported in 1889 in the "Sites Relating to the Underground Railroad, Abolitionism, African American Life by Auburn Historic Resources Review Board Cayuga County Historian's Office" the following:

"Luke Freeman's father, Harry Freeman, was a childhood friend (as well as a slave [Incorrect, Harry was an indentured servant.]) of John Hardenburgh, white founder of Auburn. In 1889, Michael S. Myers remembered Harry Freeman as 'a darkie of the deepest dye, who lived amongst us to a good old age, (said to be 100) and was always foremost in wild adventures, or rather relating them. He will be remembered by our old citizens as an original character, whose ruling passion was to tell big stories, and great devotion to the Hardenbergh family.'"

11

BUILDING THE FREEMAN FAMILY

John's remains had been placed in its proper place of repose in North Street Cemetery, and Martina and the children were adjusting to a new life without John with the spiritual and physical support of the Freemans.

Uncle Harry and Aunt Kate were how the Hardenbergh children knew Harry and Kate. Harry spent a great deal of time with John Herring Hardenbergh. He was incorporated into the Freeman Clan. When Harry was teaching his boys about wilderness life, John Herring was right there with them. Kate spent a great deal of time just making herself available to share the Word of God and be a sounding board for Martina. Kate even showed Martina a few approaches in the kitchen, even her famous rhubarb pie. Martina was particularly fond of the variation of the pie that had berries in it.

Everything was progressing on God's timetable for the Hardenberghs and Freemans after their tragic loss of John. A remarkable thing that occurred after John Hardenbergh's death was the transformation of Harry Jr. Harry Jr. and Uncle John were extremely close. Uncle John had intervened on many occasions between Harry Jr. and his no-nonsense father Harry Sr. Uncle John always had a place for Harry to stay and something for him to do every time the volcano of emotions erupted at the top of the hill at New Guinea.

Uncle John's death and his witnessing of that event had refocused Harry Jr.'s commitment to God, as well as his attitude and his relationship with his father. He committed himself to work diligently with his Dad to build the Freeman family businesses. He and Platt became Harry's major work supporters. Their dad felt like Moses with Aaron and Hur, holding his arms up in order to win the battle.

Luke was part of that "triad of support" of Harry Jr., Luke, and Platt available to Harry Sr. Luke was a visionary and a gifted interactor with people. You could say that Harry Freeman Sr.'s "triad of Support" were the original "undercover brothers." Caroline was Kate's admirer with the same disposition as her mother and learned everything Kate had to offer.

The Freemans' philosophy was to "stay out of the eyes of the white public. People only need to know on a 'need to know basis.'"

White historians have no accounting of Harry Jr.'s exploits and contribution to the Auburn community. Platt (P.R.) and his wife Mary's roles as operators of one of the most important stations along the Underground Railroad is only identified in three accounts, a passage in Kate Clifford Larson's book (2004) *Bound for the Promise Land, Harriet Tubman (Portrait of an American Hero)*, the great Underground Railroad conductor William Still's book (1872) *The Underground Railroad*, and a compilation (with a few errors) (2004-05) by *Sites Relating to the Underground Railroad, Abolitionism, African American Life*, sponsored by Auburn Historic Resources Review Board Cayuga County Historian's Office.

I have chosen the latter, the compilation, to present Platt Roundtree (P.R.) Freeman's and Morgan Lewis (Luke) Freeman's White historical information in perspective, with their errors.

Platt Roundtree (P.R.) Freeman:

"William Still, who kept the main safe house in Philadelphia, recorded one specific instance of an Underground Railroad event in which P.R Freeman, probably either Luke Freeman or his son Burgett Freeman [ERROR ALERT—Wrong, that's why the term 'probably' was used. P.R. Freeman is my great-great-grandfather Platt Roundtree Freeman], were involved in 1858. Nat and Lizzy Amby escaped from Cambridge, Maryland, to Auburn and wrote a letter back to inform their family. Their story is best told in the words of William Still and in Nat Amby's own letter. As Still reported,

"Nat is no ordinary man. Like a certain other Nat known to history, his honest and independent bearing in every respect was that of a natural hero. He was full black, and about six feet high; of powerful physical proportions, and of more than ordinary intellectual capacities. With the strongest desire to make the Port of Canada safely he had resolved to be 'carried back,' if attacked by the slave hunters, 'only as a dead man.' He was held to service by John Muir, a wealthy farmer and the owner of 40 or 50 slaves. 'Muir would drink and was generally devilish.' Two of Nat's sisters and one of his brothers had been 'sold away to Georgia by him.' Therefore, admonished by threats and fears of having to pass through the same fiery furnace, Nat was led to consider the U. G. R. R. scheme {Under Ground Rail Road}. It was through the marriage of Nat's mistress to his present owner that he came into Muir's hands. 'Up to the time of her death,' he had been encouraged to 'hope' that he would be 'free,' indeed, he was assured by her 'dying testimony that the slaves were not to be sold.' But regardless of the promises and will of his departed wife, Muir soon extinguished all hopes of freedom from that quarter. But not believing that God had put one man here to 'be the servant of another—to work,' and get none of the benefit of his labor, Nat armed himself with a good pistol and a big knife, and taking his wife with him, bade adieu forever to bondage. Observing that Lizzie (Nat's wife) looked pretty decided and resolute, a member of the committee remarked, 'Would your wife fight for freedom?' 'I have heard her say she would wade through blood and tears for her freedom,' said Nat, in the most serious mood.

"The following advertisement from The Cambridge Democrat of Nov. 4, speaks for itself-

> "$300 REWARD.--Ran away from the subscriber, on Saturday night last, 17th inst., my negro woman Lizzie, about 28 years old. She is medium sized, dark complexion, good looking, with rather a down look. When spoken to replies quickly. She was well dressed, wearing a red and green blanket shawl, and carried with her a variety of clothing. She ran off in company with her husband, Nat Amby (belonging to John Muir, Esq.), who is about 6 feet in height, with slight impediment in his speech, dark chestnut color, and a large scar on the side of his neck.

"I will give the above reward if taken in this County, or one-half of what she sells for if taken out of the County or State. In either case to be lodged in Cambridge Jail Cambridge, Oct. 21, 1857. ALEXANDER H. BAYLY. P. S.-For the apprehension of the above-named negro man Nat, and delivery in Cam- bridge Jail, I will give $500 reward. JOHN MUIR.

"Now since Nat's master has been introduced in the above order it seems but appropriate that Nat should be heard too; consequently the following letter is inserted for what it is worth:

"AUBURN, June 10th, 1858:

"MR. WILLIAM STILL-Sir, will you be so Kind as to write a letter to affey White in strawberry alley in Baltimore city on the point Say to her at nat Ambey that I wish to Know from her the Last Letar that Joseph Ambie and Henry Ambie two Brothers and Ann Warfield a couisin of them two boys I state above I would like to hear from my mother sichy Ambie you will Please write to my mother and tell her that I am well and doing well and state to her that I perform my Relissius dutys and I would like to hear from her and want to know if she is performing her Relissius dutys yet and send me word from all her children I left behind say to affey White that I wish her to write me a Letter in Hast my wife is well and doing well and my nephew is doing well Please tell affey White when she writes to me to Let me know where Joseph and Henry Ambie is "Mr. Still Please Look on your Book and you will find my name on your Book They was eleven of us children and all when we came through and I feal interrested about my Brothers I have never heard from them since I Left home you will Please Be Kind annough to attend to this Letter When you send the answer to this Letter you will Please send it to P. R. Freeman Auburn City Cayuga County New York Yours Truly

   NAT AMBIE"

Morgan Lewis (Luke) Freeman:

"Luke Freeman probably [He did.] grew up with his par-ents and other family members in New Guinea. He be-came, said his obituary, first a gunsmith, a trade that he followed with 'considerable success,' and then a barber. He did it well enough to purchase two pieces of property from Abijah Fitch on June 5, 1847, and July 1, 1848, the first for $250 on Lot 31 Cumpston Street (now Lincoln Street) and the second for $250 on the northeast corner of Cumpston Lane and South Street, next to the Presbyterian Church and just north and ac-ross from the Seward House.

   "Whether Freeman kept his barbershop here, or whether he used these lots for some other purpose is not known. An advertisement in the Auburn Daily Advertiser on January 9, 1851, noted that Luke Freeman's barbershop was located in the American Hotel on Genesee Street. By 1857, the city directory noted that Freeman had moved his barbershop to a new site. 113 Genesee Street, at the northeast corner of Genesee and State Street.

"In 1859, Luke Freeman appears to have had a stroke. He remained paralyzed until his death on April 9, 1863. His obituary noted that

"Luke had become almost 'an institution' in Auburn, not only on account of his general cleverness and usefulness, but as the leading sympathizer with his race yet in bondage. For more than 29 years his house was a refuge of the fleeing fugitive, derisively {sarcastically} called 'The Underground Railroad Depot.' His practical sympathy for those unfortunates won him esteem of all those who were cognizant of his labors." [Auburn Advertiser and Union]

"His funeral, held at his house, attracted hundreds of Auburn citizens, both back and white. As the Auburn Daily Advertiser noted:

'The funeral of Luke Freeman took place yesterday from his residence in Court Street, and was one of the most solemn and imposing scenes of the times. Luke was the 'Uncle Tom' {It was meant as a compliment because Uncle Tom, in Harriet Beecher Stowe's book Uncle Tom's Cabin (1852), was a kind and caring man to

people of all color. His name took on a derogatory con-
nation of "compromise with White people" during the
Jim Crow Era and the Civil Rights Movement.} of his
people here—clever, kind, generous, good. He had been
the benefactor, indeed, of hundreds and perhaps thousands of his race. He had been so good in so many ways
the white folks had forgotten that he was black. He had
most emphatically conquered the prejudices existing
against his race.'

"To the everlasting credit of the white people of our
city they turned out in large numbers to Luke's funeral,
just as they usually do to the funerals of our most re-
spectable white citizens. Five of our most distinguished
clergymen officiated. Rev. Dr. Hawley read the Scrip-
tures, Rev. Mr. Ives offered the prayer, Rev. Mr. Fowler
and Rev. Mr. Hosmer delivered short discourses, Rev.
Dr. Huntington pronounced the benediction. And all the
services were deeply impressive and solemn. [Cayuga
County Historian's Office]

"Fourteen carriages full of people, white and black,
followed his remains to the grave in the old North street
cemetery, where he was buried with his ancestors. Rev.
Dr. Hawley addressed the people and invoked benediction there.

It seemed to be a tribute to remarkable goodness on
the part of an old colored Patriarch, in which all our
people (?) to join. There was interest in the fact that he

had been a slave [Incorrect. John Hardenbergh registered Luke as the baby of his servants. White people interpreted it as meaning slave. His parents, Harry and Kate Freeman, had always been Free.]. There was interest, also, in the fact that the surviving mother of his wife was born in Africa over a hundred years ago, and remembers the evacuation of New York by the British and the entry there of Geo. Washington, whose person and deportment she minutely describes. She remembers the time when Sinclair Smith, of this country, was U.S. Marshal, and when he arrested certain parties for the complicity in the treasonable projects of Aaron Burr. There was more of interest, however in the fact that he had risen above the clouds which hung over his race, and conquered the prejudices of the people against those of his color. As he himself had said in his lifetime, 'Nobody in Auburn regarded him as a Negro—they respected him as Luke.'

"Well, death reduces all distinctions created by wealth or color: and none of our most courtly aristocrats went to their graves with any higher honors then were borne by good old Luke. He was a good man. Peace to his ashes." [Auburn Daily Advertiser, April 11, 1863. From Seward House scrapbooks. Transcribed by Seward House.]

[It was necessary to establish some basic universal information before continuing this Epic.]

Harry was growing older now and was depending more and more on his children. Harry Jr. was working hard to guide the businesses that his mother Kate had cultivated along the Genesee Pike. Now with the inclusion of the Seneca Turnpike and the efforts of building a water canal north of Auburn, Harry, Jr. was spending more time in the Seneca Lake area than he was at New Guinea. The Freemans, through Harry Jr., handled the menial jobs and supplying of laborers to conduct those menial tasks, such as latrine maintenance, removal, and relocation, washing, cooking, and cleaning. This was making New Guinea a great place for Free and Runaway Blacks to live and have employment opportunities.

Caroline was the reincarnation of her grandmother, Chinwe. She was no nonsense, extremely bright, and very astute about the world around her. Everything her mother and father offered her in building her character and developing a way to live in this world, Caroline absorbed like a sponge. Kate "homeschooled" her children and the children of New Guinea. By the time Caroline, "Puddin" was her family nickname, was twelve, she was instructing the youngest children by herself. Puddin's cooking skills were developing so fast that her daddy couldn't tell whether it was her or her mother preparing the meal on occasions.

It was Caroline who stayed at the Hardenberg's home for two months after the death of Uncle John, in order to make sure everything was operating correctly within the house for Aunt Martina and the children. Puddin was quite an attraction at New Guinea and around Auburn. Many a young fellow were interested in courting young Puddin, but one look from Kate or Harry made it clear to proceed with right Godly Intentions or suffer consequences that could have a life-altering or ending affect.

One young man who had grown up with Caroline, named Aaron Denum, was the second best student next to Caroline and had been in love with her since the age of eight. He was determined to have Puddin as his wife, and years later, this reality would be achieved.

Kate and Caroline had other brilliant students. One of major note was John De Puy. John married Kate and Harry's granddaughter. John was a dazzling young man. Kate would often tell Harry that if it wasn't for white folks' stupid racism, John could be the governor of the state or the president of these whole United States. John was so gifted that during the murder trial of his brother-in-law, William Freeman (1846), William Seward said this about him:

The testimony of Freeman's brother-in-law John De Puy so moved Seward that he quoted it in his closing argument. Seward exclaimed that he had heard the greatest of American orators, as well as Europeans Daniel O'Connell and Sir Robert Peel, but John De Puy had 'excelled them all in eloquence.' De Puy testified: "They have made William Freeman what he is, a brute beast; they don't make anything else of any of our people but brute beasts; but when we violate their laws, then they want to punish us as if we were men.' If any witness inspired a degree of self-consciousness among the jury, it was John De Puy. ["Defence of William Freeman," in the Works of William H Seward, vol. 1 ed. George E. Baker (New York: Redfield, 1853); "The William Freeman Murder Trial" by Andrew W. Arpey]

Morgan "Luke" and Platt "P.R." were as close as two peas in a pod. They communicated openly and honestly with each other. They knew their prospective roles within the family and embraced their roles with vim and vigor. Platt was determined to provide his father the support needed to expand the Freeman businesses and garner the respect as a God-Fearing, good man in the face of society's hateful racist attitudes. With Platt's skillful marketing approaches, the Freemans had business contracts with many of Auburn's and the surrounding vicinities', beside Uncle John's, mills; the Freemans provided staffing and other ancillary services to the following enterprises:

- S Cumpston Flour & Saw Mills
- Standards Farm
- Roger's Quarry
- Phelps Stone Quarry

- Leonard & Warden Flour Mill
- Paper Mill (On Clarks Ville St.)
- Cotton Factory (near the Falls)
- The Brewery (R. Watson)
- J.B. Dill's Stone Quarry
- B. White Shop and more....

New Guinea had become a community of over thirty (30) buildings of various sizes with the larger units housing twelve (12) to fifteen (15) individuals comfortably. Harry Jr. was now talking to Platt about the increasing opportunities on the completion of the Cayuga-Seneca Canal and the fact construction was almost completed on the extension that would connect the Cayuga-Seneca Canal with the Erie Canal.

Harry Jr. told Luke and Platt that "Big Man," Daniel Hughes, said hello. "Big Man" was a childhood friend of Platt and Luke, though Daniel lived forty miles North of Auburn in the Oswego area. Harry and Kate's travels throughout the region had brought them across a small settlement of Africans, some free, some runaways, all striving outside the eye of White folks between Fulton and Oswego.

The Hughes Family made its living on the great sea called Lake Ontario. Their son Daniel was a year younger than Luke, which made him the perfect playmate for Platt and Luke. Even though they were forty miles apart, Luke and Platt spent a great deal of time at the Hughes' home, and Big Man did likewise at the Freemans' home. Daniel was entitled to that nickname "Big Man" because he was two to three times bigger than any child his age (When he reached adulthood, he would stand 6'8" tall and weigh three hundred pounds). Now Big Man was working with Harry Jr. on the canal extensions utilizing a barge to move material and supplies. On occasions, Big Man helped the Freemans to move runaways closer to the water escape out of Oswego in order to escape to Canada.

Big Man had told Harry Jr. that as soon as his work was done on the canal extension he was moving to Pennsylvania. He had discovered that the Washington, DC/Baltimore area was in a constant need of lumber. Daniel was moving to the Williamsport, Pennsylvania, area to build a barge and transport lumber down the Susquehanna River to Havre De Grace on the Chesapeake Bay. From there lumber could be easily transported by boat to Washington or Baltimore. Needed and wanted supplies and goods could then be brought back to central Pennsylvania. More importantly, Daniel "Big Man" Hughes would become an important component of the Underground Railroad and a major confidant to Luke Freeman and his operation as a prominent leader of the Underground Railroad.

Platt was now the chief operating person for the Freemans' enterprises out of New Guinea. Harry settled into a role of consulting and monitoring and enjoying his son's ascension to leadership. Harry could now spend more time praising and worshipping the Lord. When August and Tootie Brown joined the New Guinea community they explained how they worshipped the Lord down South. They told Harry that they would go into the woods and clear an area to build a "praise house." That way they could worship the Lord in a fashion more comfortable to them. Harry told them, "Well, you won't have to travel to the woods here! We'll just build a 'Praise House' on this land God has given us!"

Harry and August conducted the church services on Sunday, and Harry led the Bible studies on Tuesday and Thursday. Three times Harry had to expand the "praise house" in order to accommodate the population explosion at New Guinea. The congregation at New Guinea's praise house would compose the basis of the AME Zion Church in Auburn.

Luke, from his travel through the country, had told his father about a church that was designed to minister and share the Word of God to Black people. Mother Zion, or the Freedom Church, as it was called by Blacks, was officially named the African Methodist Episcopal Zion Church or the AME Zion Church. Harry and Kate were enthralled with the idea of being able to worship in an organized church that didn't have restrictions and folkways as predetermined criteria for Blacks to participate.

The one thing they missed the most from England was the religious freedom they had enjoyed. They queried Luke about the Freedom Church and what they needed to do to have a church in Auburn. Luke proceeded to explain to them that Mother Zion was playing a major role in bringing people together that were doing the same thing that the Freemans were doing with runaway slaves, plus bringing abolitionists together to orchestrate their efforts.

Luke excitedly asked, "Do you remember Bell, the young slave girl that was owned by Uncle John's relatives?"

Harry responded, "Of course, Old Colonel Johannes Hardenberg, Uncle John's uncle and Jacob's daddy. Poor baby, he had left Bell in his will to that shiftless Charlie, his other son. I always wondered about that boy, Charlie Hardenbergh. He never exhibited the focus that was a Hardenbergh trait. Uncle John spent years trying to convince his uncle, the hard charging Col. Johannes Hardenbergh, his namesake, that slavery was wrong and violated the Word and Mandate of God."

Kate sat there looking down and shaking her head in remorse as Harry continued, "Little Bell had the most intense eyes I have ever seen. It was like she was looking down your mouth, snatching every word that was coming out and chewing on them. She could unnerve the strongest of men. I've always wondered what happened to her." Kate, wiping tears from her eyes, said, "I loved that little girl. I prayed and prayed that God would make a way for that child to be free! I asked Him over and over again if He would let me have her. I guess God had other plans for her."

Luke put his arms around his mother's shoulder and said gently, "Mama, she's free. I ran into her at the National Negro Convention in Philadelphia."

"You talking about that conference you went to at Mother Bethel Church?" interjected Harry.

"Yes, Dad, the one that Hezekiel Grice invited me to attend. Bishop Allen had told Hezekiel that we would be delighted to host his conference at his church in Philadelphia," responded Luke.

"Your friend Hezekiel took his first National Negro Conference to Bishop Richard Allen's African Methodist Episcopal Bethel Church? To the founder of our first Black denomination in this country? I'll say, there was no way that boy was going to control his own conference," pontificated Harry.

"Yeah, Dad, you're right; Hezekiel Grice gave the opening address, and Bishop Allen took over after that. By the time we finished identifying, discussing, and reducing the issues to be addressed, Bishop Richard Allen was voted the first president of the American Society of Free People of Colour.

"Hezekiel was so despondent about the internal political maneuvering at what was supposed to be 'his conference' that, within the month, he had packed all his belongings and moved to Canada. But that's not why I brought up the conference," exclaimed Luke.

"I know, I know, but did you tell the good Bishop I said hello?" Harry smirked.

"I did, and he told me to tell you and mom he said hello. Mom, he said nobody can make a rhubarb pie like you. Bishop Allen said to tell you thank you for the pie and that *'you put your foot in it!'*

Kate laughed and said, "Good old Bishop Allen."

Regaining his resolve and recapturing his determination to share the news about Bell, Luke made eye contact with his brother Platt who smiled and nodded his head. Luke knew what that meant. Their parents had always felt guilty about not being able to secure Bell's freedom from the Hardenberghs. Any discussion about Bell sullied the atmosphere, taking Harry and Kate back to the loss of their child. So, avoidance and deflection were Harry's "modus operandi" in order to spare his wife emotional turmoil.

Luke's information about Bell, if his Dad wasn't in deflect-mode, would have been a heartwarming story of God's Intervention and Bell's perseverance, but repeated emotional subjugations automatically caused his father to go into deflect-mode in his normal attempt to protect his wife, their mother.

Mom and Dad were heading to the front door to get some air when Platt stated with authority, "You are not responsible for Chipo's death."

Harry whirled around and overran Platt's personal space with a glance of hatred unrefined that no child of Kate and Harry Freeman had witnessed before and snarled, "What do you know about losing a child? What do you know about your loved one being degraded and abused, *in your presence?*"

Platt, not flinching nor backing away from this "personal assault" of his father, responded with the same authority that initiated this encounter, "Only what Mom and you taught us about God." At that moment his son's eyes became a pair of reflective pools of familiarity of himself, causing Harry to retreat from his righteous assault.

Harry turned and grabbed Kate's hand, who for the first time in Platt's and Luke's existence and historical remembrance, had abandon her pillar of strength image and quietly exerted, "We'll be back shortly," and walked out the door.

Luke spun his brother around and blurted, "No, you didn't!"

"No, I didn't what?" responded Platt.

"No, you didn't go there with Dad! All I wanted to do was tell them that Bell was free. That she changed her name to Sojourner Truth. That she sued a White man down South to gain custody of her son. That she was becoming a major voice in the abolitionist movement and suffragette activities, but most important, she became obedient to the Word of God and was worshipping the Lord in the AME Church," exclaimed Luke. "That's all I wanted to do."

Platt smiled. "I am happy that Bell, I mean Sojourner, is free. I thank God Sojourner is doing so well, and I look forward to spending some time with her in the future, but there was a bigger, more deep-rooted issue that God wanted addressed."

"Luke, Mom and Dad have always taught us 'that accepting God's forgiveness meant you were completely forgiven.' They have forgotten that meant yourself also. Over and over they would recite, 'Only God has a heaven and hell. If you accept God's Forgiveness you won't need to forgive yourself.' The devil uses Chipo's death over and over again to make our strong parents in the Lord, weak and confused. I guess the Lord got tired of it and decided to use us to bring it to an end. We'll see what God says."

Luke, in complete resolve and support of his brother, gasped and shared, "You're right, Platt."

"Dad and Mom's overriding want has been to bring organized religion for Black folks to Auburn. The devil, masquerading as light, always seemed to get them distracted from that goal. It never fails that Satan interjects something that makes them feel responsible for our sister's death, as if it was their fault. I'm glad God used us and that you followed God's direction in confronting Dad. Platt, you have always been the one deeply spirited rooted, with no care for acclaim in this world. I'm glad you're my brother."

Harry and Kate wandered out back behind the praise house and sat in their favorite spot overlooking the Owasco Outlet River. The Outlet was a little cavernous at this juncture, but this had always been where Kate and Harry came to seek God's direction and peace. "Kate, I don't know what happened. I was in Platt's face filled with a raged that I hadn't experience since the 'Beach of Sorrow,'" lamented Harry. Harry fell on his face petitioning God's forgiveness and guidance. With the rushing Outlet screaming against the rocks and twist in its path, silence fell over the Freemans for what seemed like, time without end.

It had been a time without end. A time without end of feeling guilty for their child's death. A time without end for allowing her daughter to be ripped from her arms and not dying in an attempt to save her life. A time without end of feeling less than a man for what happened to his wife and his daughter. A time without end where Satan was accusing them and belittling them. A time without end were "the Accuser" wasn't blaming them for their children's problems. A time without end that the Devil wasn't lying to them and creating a fog of war to limit their reception of the Peace that God had for them.

The overwhelming silence was not broken by the roar below of the river but by Kate's declaration, "No More! No more will we allow the Devil to hold us responsible for the wrong doings of other human beings with free will!" Kate gathered up her husband, and they sat holding each other until they knew it was time to return home and make amends with their sons.

12

LIFE IN AUBURN

Platt thought his hands were busy with the day to day operations of the Freeman businesses. His sister Caroline married Aaron Denum, and Aaron had proven to be "a man of worth." Platt had also taken a bride also. Her name was Mary.

Mary had been a slave to Beatrice Sange, a seamstress in Washington DC. One Thursday while Beatrice and Mary were working on a project in Havre de Grace, Maryland, Mary saw the tallest human being that she had ever seen in her life, and he was Black like her. She approached him, seeking information about the local worship house for Blacks. She had already been in Havre de Grace long enough to thirst for a Black worship House. She approached this man who reminded her of the Bible and its reference to "Giants in the Land" and the Greek literature that she had read that lavished attention on Titans and softly asked, "Excuse me, sir, I was wondering if you could help me?"

Doffing his hat, Daniel Hughes responded, "How may I be of service?"

"I'm here in Havre de Grace with my mistress working on a sewing project. I would really like to praise the Lord in a Black worship house this Sunday. Mistress Beatrice's choice for Sunday worship lacks the flavor I need to express my love and appreciation to God."

Nodding his head to the affirmative Daniel Hughes replied, "I know what you mean. I can be of service to you, miss, in that matter." Daniel explained where the Morning Star Praise House was located and told Mary he would see her there since his cargo that he was to take back up the Susquehanna River to Williamsport, Pennsylvania, was delayed in Baltimore.

Sunday could not come early enough for Mary. Sunday was her only day that she did not have to account for her whereabouts to Mistress Beatrice. Her one day of freedom from a woman who bathed in the exploitations of her skills but could not and would not acknowledge Mary's humanity, while faking belief and allegiance to the One True God!

Mary enjoyed the worship service at Morning Star and the fellowship meal afterwards. She was feeling a little guilty for not having contributed anything to the meal, but Daniel calmed her angst. "The people here get great joy in receiving strangers and making new friends in the old way, by breaking bread. Mary, where are you from, and do you have a last name?" asked Daniel.

Mary smirked and said, "I don't know where I'm from, Virginia, Maryland, I don't know. I was sold to Beatrice Sange as a small child. I don't even know who my parents are. Every time I would ask a grown person whose charge I was under if they were my mother, they would say no. As far as a last name, I will not take one until I am free!"

Silenced stalked their conversation for a long moment then she continued, "I learned to be a seamstress even better than Mistress Beatrice. I've longed to be free my entire life and then some." The both broke out into laughter. After regaining her decorum, she said, "I couldn't be free, but I work to do what I can for others. I take the end piece of the bolts of fabric that we purchase and other material that Mistress Beatrice or our customers don't want and make clothing for runaway slaves coming through Washington on the Underground Railroad. It helps them to blend in and discard their rags. I almost got caught on several occasions by slave catchers delivering clothes to safe houses. Once those white folks saw the expensive material and the quality of the work, they knew that my lie had to be true."

Daniel chuckled and asked, "Did you ever try to runaway yourself?"

Mary looked stunned as she gathered herself to respond, "I never thought of how to become free! I've been just like that elephant Mr. Bailey has! Oh my God, I've been keeping myself in slavery!" A farmer from New Jersey named Hachaliah Bailey had bought a baby elephant named Old Bet. Mr. Bailey was going around the country showing off Old Bet for money. Every time he would come to Washington, he would have us make a new dazzling outfit for his elephant exhibition. When he first visited our shop, Old Bet was small. I watched him put a colorful stake in the ground and anchor an equally colorful chain to the elephant's collar. The young elephant would struggle against the stake and chain but eventually realized that she could not free herself and calmed down. By the time Mr. Bailey came back for another outfit Old Bet the elephant was huge.

"Mr. Bailey used the same stake and chain that he had used when Old Bet was small to now secure the grown elephant. I knew it was the same stake because on their first visit, as my fear turned to curiosity about Old Bet and elephants in general, Mr. Bailey let me write my name on Old Bet's stake. Hachaliah Bailey always has treated me kindly.

"Now with Old Bet being so big, fear started creeping back into my spirit. I asked him with great concern for my wellbeing, 'Is that stake and chain going to hold Old Bet in place?'

"He chuckled and warmly stated, 'When Old Bet was small, she would fight against that stake until one day Old Bet realized she could not get away from it. In that moment of acquiescence, she never struggled against that stake again. Old Bet accepted the stake's authority over her. There is no way a stake, a pole, or your building itself could keep Old Bet from being free without her submission to her plight. Mary, take a close look at the stake again. It still has your name on it. It's the same stake.'"

As Mary leaned on the table she looked up at Daniel and calmly said, "He didn't have to tell me about the stake. I already knew it was the same stake of bondage, but I didn't want to accept it. I understand now that I have been suffering from the plight of submission to slavery which is similar to Old Bet's submission to the stake." She looked at Daniel and said firmly, "From this day forward I'm putting more effort in to obtaining my freedom then maintaining this position of bondage."

"Are you sure that's what you want to do?" quizzed Daniel carefully. "Freedom is not easy; it requires a great deal of personal effort and sacrifice," he added.

"Mr. Hughes, I will be Free!" Mary snapped. "If I must walk, eat swamp food, crawl on my belly, or fight tooth and nail, I'm getting my freedom. No 'stake of slavery' is ever holding me back again!"

Daniel Hughes was rubbing his chin and marveling at the resolve this young Black woman was exhibiting when he said, "Mary, I think I can help you."

He first told her that his family and friends called him "Big Man," for obvious reasons. Big Man then explained how he had been working on the Underground Railroad as a station ferrying runaway slaves North on his barge and hiding them in caves near his property outside Williamsport, Pennsylvania. Mary looked amazed that freedom could be so close at hand that she offered an immediate prayer of gratitude to God for this opportunity.

Mary, being a seamstress, was big on precision and details. She told Big Man that she had heard talk about stations and terminals on the Underground Railroad, but she didn't understand the difference or importance of those two things. Big Man explained, "Stations on the Underground Railroad were stopovers where runaway slaves could be hidden, fed, clothed, and rested before they continued their journey North. Usually the stopovers were brief since those communities were not suitable for protecting runaways against slave catchers."

"The Underground Railroad terminals are stations that offer runaways and option of settling there or moving on to Canada. Right now, we have four terminals in the east, Philadelphia, New York, Boston, and New Guinea in Auburn, New York. Three of the terminals, Boston, New York, and Philadelphia, have Vigilant Committees that kept the slave catchers in check. Auburn has the Freemans and their Tree Leopards."

"Tree Leopards? Are those some type of animals they trained to protect Blacks from slave catchers?" asked Mary.

Big Man chuckled and said, "Ma and Pa Freeman have never been slaves. They came from Africa by way of England to the colonies before we were a country. Harry and Kate Freeman, that's their names, started a free slave colony on fourteen acres of land called New Guinea in Auburn, New York. Soon, free and runaway Blacks were flocking to this haven not far from the Canadian Border. The Vigilant Committees in Boston, New York, and Philadelphia were a mix of Whites and Blacks; sometimes they would get overzealous in their righteousness and create serious problems for the Underground Railroad Movement.

"Ma and Pa Freeman kept the Tree Leopards completely Black and secretive. They taught every new arrival to New Guinea the ancient ways of fighting and stealth. Harry had been the captain of a chieftain's elite group of warriors known as the Tree Leopards. Kate's mother had been a leader in one of the most feared military units in Africa, the Agooji Warriors. Their track record for protecting runaway slaves was impeccable. They didn't have a name for what they were doing until I told them that it was called the Underground Railroad. They just did what they did in the name of the Lord."

Mary was enthralled with the information Big Man was sharing with her asked, "Are you related to the Freemans?"

"No," he said looking up, "I grew up about forty miles north of the Freemans. Two of their boys are very close childhood friends, Luke and Platt. The Freemans are like my second family."

"That sounds like the kind of place I would like to settle. How do I get there?" Mary asked.

Big Man smiled looked around to assure himself that no one was eavesdropping and bent his six feet, eight-inch frame down to whispering level to Mary and said, "I can help you with that."

Daniel "Big Man" Hughes explained in great detail to Mary his role in moving runaway slaves North. He told Mary that she was going to dress as a boy and keep her mouth shut. "You will be mute but not deaf, and your name will be Mark." Daniel looked around to assure their privacy was still intact and said, "The supplies that I've been waiting for will be here by Friday. You can't say goodbye to anyone. You can't pack a bag or do anything out of the ordinary that would bring attention to yourself.

"After you've finished your duties and had your supper Saturday evening, meet me at the dock at 9:30. We will be leaving as soon as you get there. We will have

Saturday night and Sunday before your mistress will even be aware that you are missing."

"What harm would it do if I say goodbye to Adisa?" Mary retorted. "She's a little Black girl I've been teaching to sew and truly she is like family to me!"

Big Man rose up and expanded to his full width and height and said with great authority, "Look here, white folks are very cagey, and Black folks are very envious; if your daily itinerary is altered one iota, your mistress will have slave catchers watching your every move in order to destroy the Underground Railroad and me. Plus, if Black folks get wind of you leaving, somebody is going to run to the white folks trying to improve their status. You Change Nothing! You Say Goodbye to No One! You Don't Bring Nothing! That's the price of your freedom. UNDERSTOOD?"

Sheepishly she nodded and said, "Yes, sir."

They left Havre de Grace at 10:00 and started their journey to Mary's freedom. Big Man told Mary that he would personally take her to Ma and Pa Freeman. He informed her he hadn't been home to see his people in the Oswego area in several years. "So, we are going to kill two birds with one stone." He chuckled. "It's about 160 miles from here to Williamsport and about another 160 miles to Auburn, but the most dangerous part is going to be the next eighty or so miles till we get north of Harrisburg. We'll rest up at my home for a few days; if I get wind of slave catchers in the area, I'll have to hide you in one of the caves. Otherwise, we rest up and take the barge to Barton, New York, leave it there, then take a wagon north to Auburn by the Auburn road."

The entire trip was fully uneventful. No interruptions or queries about who they were and what they were doing. Big Man's reputation made way for his girth.

After several weeks, they arrived at the home of Ma and Pa Freeman at New Guinea in Auburn. After warm embraces from Big Man to all the Freemans present, he turned and introduced Mary, "Ma, Pa, this is Mary, the seamstress a free woman now."

Mary curtsied in her men's clothes issued a soul exhibiting grin and said, "It's an honor and a pleasure to meet you."

Harry and Kate returned Mary's salutation as did the other members of the family that where in the room, except for Platt. Platt looked like he had been kicked senseless by his mule. Harry turned to his son smirking said, "Son are you going to greet our guest?"

Platt was trying to gather himself and was having trouble formulating what he thought would be the right response blurted out, "Yep. Hi."

Harry knew what was happening to his boy. He had been struck by the love bolt. The same love bolt that struck him years ago in Africa when he first saw Rehema, the mother of his children, Kate Freeman. The cobwebs and disorientation were clearing from Platt's head, and he immediately advanced to within close proximity of Mary and delicately took her hand kissed it and said, "It is with great pleasure that I welcome you to New Guinea, and I look forward to sharing knowledge of our community and the Auburn area, at your convenience."

Mary, not being used to such attention being directed in her path, found her spirit fluttering and replied with honey-sweetened tones, "I would truly enjoy that, Mr. Freeman."

"No, no," retorted Platt, "It's Platt, or P.R. to those I'm close with."

Mary thought to herself, "Could it be that God has given me my freedom and a love to fulfill my being?"

Well, the rest is history. Mary married Platt and became Mrs. Mary Freeman. She opened a little seamstress shop on the New Guinea property. Mary mended and sewed clothing for many of the residents of Auburn and Cayuga County. Even more important it was a place to bring used clothing for the residents of New Guinea.

Platt and Mary had New Guinea operating like a well-oiled machine. Not only was New Guinea doing well, but residents of the free slave colony were beginning to move into the general community and were productive members of the community.

Platt and Luke told their parents that a name had been given for what they had been doing for runaway slaves for decades. They call it the Underground Railroad. Kate broke out into laughter and turned to Harry and quipped, "Well, Conductor, all you need is a train whistle. I think I'll get you one for Christmas." Everybody in the room was rolling with laughter while making train whistle sounds.

From the corner of the room Luke, gasping for air from rolling on the floor with laughter, hollered, "Hey, Dad, does that mean you have to learn Morse Code. 'Dit dit da dit dit,'" more laughter.

"Alright, alright," bellowed Harry. "Y'all had a good laugh, but don't get carried away. I don't know nothing about a railroad above ground or underground. All I know is that as long as this country of ours condones slavery of fellow human beings, we Freemans will do everything we can with God's help to free those slaves." There was a chorus of "Amens," and everyone got back to work.

Work was what Mary and Platt's world centered around, but one activity that was closer to their heart was the plight of runaway slaves. New Guinea in Auburn, New York, was the fourth largest station and terminal in the east behind William Stills' operations in Philadelphia, the AME Zion Church's operations in New York, and William Lloyd Garrison's operations in Boston. When offers from William Stills to come to Auburn and help them establish a Vigilante Committee, Luke told him that his father appreciated the concern, but a Vigilante Committee was not necessary in Auburn. Harry had told Luke and Platt, "We only need one chef in the kitchen. You get to many people stirring the pot, ain't no telling what you end up with."

There were other issues that caused great consternation amidst the fabric of the Underground Railroad Movement. Harry would have no input or discussion about them. He saw that their meetings and discussions were destructive interference in carrying out the Lord's work. Harry had a saying when experiencing these traits in people, it kept him from getting upset and doing something that would displease his Savior, "The politics of being human hinders your work."

He knew that organizing and meeting to some degree was necessary, but they were not his cup of tea. Harry would often say, "The Devil is busy in the details. As soon as you take on the chore that the Lord has for you to address, Ole Slew Foot cranks up the petty mill and feeds it plenty of pride. It was a sure fired way not to get the Lord's Work done and create spitefulness and meanness among good caring folks."

Harry was on a roll. "Look at that young boy that came all the way from New York City to tell me how to fight back against white folks. What was his name? Wanting me to start a Committee of Vigilance to beat up hating white folks. Luke, what was that boy's name?"

"David, Dad, David Ruggles," responded Luke.

"That's it, David, David Ruggles," as Harry continued. "Nice, caring young man who was going mad with hatred. What a shame, you can't get anything done correctly if you're consumed with hatred. I tried telling him what happened to your mother and me and how we overcame with the guidance of God." Harry paused and reflected for a moment and then continued, "Poor child, he was set in his ways and didn't hear the real meaning of what I was telling him."

Kate cleared her throat, which was the universal sign that Harry had talked enough, and it was time for him to disengage. "Yes, dear," she said. "I remember David. Very idealistic young man who still had a lot to learn. Don't you worry about the committees, the conventions, the meetings, and the inner politics of the Underground Railroad Movement. You and Platt just make sure things get done here. Luke and I will attend to those other issues."

Kate and her socially active son Luke would be the architects of the Freemans' position and posture within the Underground Railroad Movement. They were the ones in the family always attempting to impact the hearts and spirits of everyone they came into contact. Harry and Platt were more pragmatic and were more likely to help you adjust your mind and re-evaluate the consequences.

Luke had ventured into an area of professional service that was vital to every member of Auburn society. He had become a gunsmith more by design than desire. He had opened a little repair shop for rifles and pistols that his wife Catherine helped him operate. He and Catherine set up shop in New Guinea and were soon addressing the firearm needs of both the black and white communities of Cayuga County. Catherine had set up a target range initially to proof their work, but eventually it became a place for raffle shoots during the holidays.

Kate had Harry Jr. custom built a wagon that would allow Freeman Firearm Repair to travel throughout the region to meet the needs of farmers and settlers in their more remote parts. The business was quite rewarding but was not completely satisfying to Luke.

Luke lamented to Catherine, "I miss human interaction! Being a gunsmith is financially rewarding but I'm tinkering with metal and wood all day long. I need to be doing something with people!"

Catherine looked at her husband and pulled him gently close to her. Peace and tranquility encased this relationship of unity. Catherine had always been the stabilizing component of the Luke Freeman family.

Catherine and Luke, practically, grew up together. Luke was three years older than Catherine, but that never impeded their play as youngsters or their budding romance in their teens. Everyone around New Guinea knew that one day Catherine and Luke would become one.

Catherine's mother Sarah had been taken as a slave in Africa. Her capture and treatment had been similar to what Kate and Harry had experienced. The major difference being that the slave ship she was on made it to the colonies. Sarah was sold to a plantation in Beaufort, South Carolina. She was then sold to a Mr. Rupprett in Virginia. It was from this location in Virginia that Sarah had escaped, via the Underground Railroad, to New York City.

Sarah was in New York City when the British retreated and General George Washington marched through the streets as the conquering hero that he had become. New York was swarming with slave catchers and unscrupulous people trying to advance themselves at someone else's expense. More and more she heard about a place Auburn, New York, that had a free slave colony called New Guinea. She packed her bag, booked passage on a wagon, and migrated to New Guinea.

Sarah's arrival at New Guinea brought Kate and Harry great delight. Sarah was from the Bantu Tribe, like them. Her Clan was the Kombe People! The three of them would spend hours behind the praise house talking and laughing in the old language and telling stories of a place and time, long passed. When they had finished their conversing, you would hear them say individually **"Ubuntu,"** then they would say collectively **"I am Because We Are."**

While rocking Luke tenderly she spoke in tones that had always brought him comfort, "It's okay. There's more to our lives than making money. Is there anything that you would like to do?"

Luke's persona quickened, and he shared something that he had never given real credence to. "I like interacting with people while I'm cutting hair. Cutting hair had been more of a past-time hobby; it was a break from hammering and tinkering all day with pistol and rifle parts."

"Well, it sounds like it to me that we are making a change!" Catherine said.

Luke proceeded to venture throughout the region letting folks know that they would no longer be providing gunsmith service to the area. There would still be a repair shop located in Auburn at New Guinea. He also informed the settlers in the outer regions that if they saw his brother Harry or one of Harry's work wagons, they could send their firearms by them to New Guinea.

Catherine would handle all the repair work, unbeknownst to customers arriving at the little shop. Her smiling face and courteous demeanor gave no indication that she was wielding the repair tools in the back room.

Eventually nobody cared who was doing the repair work. The work was well achieved, and the price was great.

Kate had known the people at the Willard Tavern a long time. Her relationship with Mr. Willard and the Willard Tavern went back to their Hardenbergh's Corners days and its importance on the Genesee Pike. The Freeman enterprises kept clean fresh sheets and towels etc. crisp and clean. Latrines were kept clean and fresh with wood chips and crushed pine needles. Cooks from New Guinea provided travelers and locals with delicious, hot food and desserts. Many a biscuit and slice of Kate's rhubarb pie eased the continuing journey of many a traveler. There was talk that the tavern was going to expand and change its name to the American Hotel.

When Luke advised his parents of his pending career change, Kate said to Luke, "Let's go visit the folks at the tavern."

Kate was able to work out a deal for Luke's barbershop. Luke would convert a back shed into a barbershop and be available to travelers and locals. When the renovations and name change took place, he would have a room in the American Hotel where he could cut hair, dust clothing, and shine shoes.

Cutting hair and barbering were not new to Luke nor to the black and white folks of Auburn. Morgan Lewis "Luke" Freeman had been barbering and cutting hair since he was fourteen. Some of the most prominent members of Auburn society. Judge Elijah Miller had built the grandiose house in Auburn across the street from the Hardenbergh estate. Luke, who was extremely personable and creative in expanding opportunities, would also carry his shoe black material and "tinker tools" to offer shoe restoration, he preferred that terminology to shoeshine, and minor cobbling repairs. No opportunity to advance economically was left unexplored with an understanding that these opportunities and blessings were a gift from God.

After what his parents had been through in their lives, it was clear to him that God had been in the mix the entire journey. He knew that happenstance and luck had nothing to do with the trials, tribulations and victories of Harry and Kate Freeman. It was all God. To that end, he made a conscious effort to help anybody of any color, anytime, anywhere, and any situation he could. All glory and obedience must be given to God.

Platt and Luke worked closely together. Every day they would meet behind the praise house to give thanks to God and to discuss what had happened during the day and any necessary responses needed from those discoveries. Platt was constantly receiving more and more free blacks and runaway slaves almost on a daily basis. Some had been field hands and Platt would locate jobs on farms or that only required manual labor. Others were skilled crafts men and women which provided the Freeman Employment Service with a bevy of artisans to be deployed in response to need.

Luke and Platt were extremely patient, a quality a black man had to possess in the racial climate of the country. They would build relationships and contacts that could take time to germinate. One such opportunity occurred when Judge Miller had hired Mr. Jeffries' contracting company to paint his house. Platt provided Mr. Jeffries laborers and handymen to assist his skilled apprentice. Platt also provided a lunch wagon so that his apprentices and other workers could take advantage of good meals. It was during this time that Platt met Brigham Young, who was working as a painter apprentice to Mr. Jeffries and enjoyed the Freeman cooking so much that he would venture up the hill to take some home occasionally. Sometime later, the Freeman business operations being run by Harry Jr. and Platt were in need of specialty buckets for some of the businesses. Platt decided to go visit the bucket company in Port Byron, New York. The first person he saw when he reached the factory was Brigham Young. They started up a cordial conversation, and Brigham was able to help resolve Platt's bucket issue.

If Luke or Platt saw a project that could be addressed by the populace of New Guinea, they would offer a remedy and a reasonably priced choice to that endeavor. That is how Mary's, Platt's wife's seamstress, abilities became so popular in Auburn and Cayuga County.

While Luke was performing his barber duties, he would hear the mistress of the house complaining about having to mail order their clothes and the condition those garments would arrive in after a long dusty, dank wagon trip to Auburn. Luke had the perfect solution and immediately shared it with Platt and Mary.

Mary was a bona fide seamstress with metropolitan talents in the middle of a fashion desert. She knew of all the best places in the Washington and Baltimore areas to purchase bolts of material and to keep abreast of the latest styles. Plus, they knew that Big Man's job kept him constantly in that area. Platt immediately got in contact with Daniel "Big Man" Hughes, and within four months Mary was offering fashion options for the ladies of upstate New York. Once again, the Finger Lakes Region could not believe the quality of work and the prices being offered by a Freeman Enterprise. It was through her seamstress abilities that Fanny Miller-Seward became a devoted customer and a friend.

Mary Freeman met a woman who was from Homer, south of Auburn, who was a writer, suffragette, and a woman's dress reform advocate named Amelia Jenks. Amelia and Mary became great associates, where Amelia would have an idea and Mary would transcribe it on paper and bring it life in the form of a trend setting garment. Amelia would eventually marry Dexter Bloomer and become Amelia Bloomer, the owner of the first women's newspaper *The Lily* and progenitor of bloomers for women.

Mary's friendship with Fanny Seward was one that was comparable to Kate Freeman's and Martina Hardenbergh's relationship. They were wives and mothers cut from the same cloth. They also had an overriding hatred of slavery.

Fanny really appreciated Mary's sewing skills and creative eye which gave them a general conversation of shared interest. Mary spent more time at the Seward house than Luke did. Luke had known and befriended William "Bill" Seward since he first came to town. He was Bill's, as he was known in the early days, barber, confidant, and confessor.

William Henry Seward came to Auburn, New York, in pursuit of the woman who had stolen his heart. Seward's sister Cornelia was attending school in Troy, New York. While visiting Cornelia, he was introduced to Frances "Fanny" Miller, the daughter of Judge Elijah Miller of Auburn. William became a frequent visitor to "Emma's School," better known as the Troy Female Seminary. Young Mr. Seward found great pleasure in traveling from Florida, New York, to Troy, New York, for the next couple of years. When Fanny graduated, she headed back to Auburn and William H Seward wasn't far behind.

William's courtship with Fanny was very serious because William Henry Seward was a very serious man.

Judge Miller was extremely impressed with his legal sharpness and his business acumen. The old judge saw a fireball of a young man who kept God first in his life and the wellbeing of all people well above his personal concern for wealth and prestige. The perfect kind of young man to complete his Fanny. He helped William to establish his law practice and introduced him to his personal barber Morgan Lewis "Luke" Freeman.

By the time the courtship was over, William and Fanny were married. William moved into the Miller estate. He and his law partners' business were flourishing in the new Exchange Building.

Seward was becoming a very recognizable political entity, but William, with his belief in God and his steadfast principles, was not willing to compromise his foundational beliefs for political advancement. He didn't like what he saw with the Masons' involvement in the political structure of American government, so he became part of the opposition to the Masons. William Seward was appalled by Andrew Jackson's attempts to alter the United States' direction of growth without consideration towards all Americans. Jackson's inhumanity toward man and might and right philosophy through "Manifest Destiny and the Spoil System" infuriated the politically developing Seward.

All through this growing public political persona of William Seward, he had his barber and friend Luke Freeman. Luke was the one that saw William as a good, caring man, not a rising political star. The Sewards found themselves developing a close relationship with the Freemans, Luke and Katherine and Platt and Mary.

They would spend time sharing how their parents came to the colonies and prospered with Uncle John Hardenbergh. Fanny and William learned from them how malicious people had enslaved their parents and how God turned evil into good for Harry and Kate.

Luke knew that William and Fanny hated slavery and wanted to be part of the solution to eliminate it. Once Luke and Platt decided it was the right time, they told the Sewards what was taking place at New Guinea to assist escaping slaves.

Immediately Fanny said, "We want to help."

Luke explained how the operations of the Underground Railroad worked and the role New Guinea played as a terminal and station. Platt explained how sometimes a large grouping of escaped slaves would arrive at once. Platt was concerned about bringing too much attention to New Guinea that could complicate their activities.

Catherine added that they needed safe houses that could accept one or two people and then filter them into New Guinea. Fanny told Catherine that they had friends of like mind and felt they could be solicited to aid in their efforts.

Mary, who had the closest relationship with Fanny Seward, shared the need for clothing and how she could discretely travel throughout the county and gather used clothing for the New Guinea residents and the new arrivals at the safe houses.

William and Fanny were delighted that they would have an active role in bringing this madness to an end. His one major concern was that this "Era of Good Feelings" in the United States was coming to an end. The country was becoming extremely mean while embracing Jacksonian Doctrines. William urged great caution on sharing this information completely with everyone. He firmly believed in "a need to know" approach, and Platt whole heartedly agreed with him.

The Freemans and Sewards agreed to work hand in hand to abolish this scourge called Slavery in the United States of America.

13

THE WINDS OF HURT

Winning a war was proving easier than agreeing on a suitable direction for a new country "of the people," "by the people," and "for the people." Coming together and following our beliefs, "In God We Trust"; "All men are created Equal"; etc., were only concepts which were having a hard time coming to fruition.

The United States of America was a toddler taking its first steps, and balance was going to be a prerequisite to developing a constructive stride. Native Americans, Blacks, women, and some white men still were not allowed to vote. The articles of confedcration had to be redeveloped, and the individual currency of each state, including their different rates, had to be eliminated. Greed, hate, selfishness, avarice, and corruption were being spread on the winds of politics. They were bccoming a source of considerable hurt and major discomfort. The winds of politics were slicing into the newly woven fabric of democracy like a rusty razor and were, at all times, trying to erode the pillars of our national existence.

The climate in the country reminded Harry and Kate of the "poison winds" in Africa which destroyed and confused their attempts to move forward. They were always providing a fog of uncertainty, but Kate and Harry had learned to protect what was the most important things in their eyes. Look down at your steps one at a time, and you will reach your goal in the face of "poison winds" or oppositions. This was the Freeman doctrine they attempted to instill in their children and grandchildren.

Even righteous causes like freeing enslaved people and obtaining the right to vote were feeling the hurt from these poison winds; however, under the direction of God and the wisdom that God had brought to them, they succeeded. Through trails, tribulations, and their acceptance to God's Will for their lives, the Freemans had been able to navigate through all of these diverse winds of hurt. Poison winds were pummeling them in every direction, but steadfast they stayed in spirit. The Freemans had committed themselves to a life of service to God and that course would not be altered.

Luke was building quite a reputation around town as the best barber and one of the nicest human beings you would ever meet of any color. His deportment and attitude were always inspiring, even to great men of God like Pastor Charles Grandison Finney and Father Nash. They were men of the Great Spiritual Revival who would stop by the American Hotel to receive grooming and inspiration from Luke whenever they were in the Auburn area either visiting the seminaries or providing a revival.

Luke was the Man! Little did all these distinguished people know the work that he and his mother Kate were putting into the Underground Railroad Movement politics and the growing Suffragette Movement.

Kate was getting older, and she knew she needed to start grooming one of her grandchildren in the ways that were important to the Freeman Family. Her choice was Ethel Freeman, her son Harry's oldest child. Ethel was a precocious child growing up. She was always uninterested in family business with no great desire for play or frivolity, like some of her siblings and cousins. She was a no-nonsense child that loved her Poppa and Nana.

Kate had assigned all suffragette concerns to Mary, Platt's wife, and Ethel while still guiding Luke's involvement with the Underground Railroad politics. The day-to-day operation of New Guinea and the Freeman Enterprises were in good hands with Harry, Harry Jr., and Platt, but the politics of both the Underground Railroad and the Suffragette activities in nearby Seneca Falls, Waterloo, and Rochester was a different subject.

The Underground Railroad Movement was a hotbed of tension based on preference of tactics, a clash of egos, and doctrines and what to do with freed slaves and free-born African Americans. Harry and Kate had always avoided participation in the first two issues. Having both served in leadership capacities in Africa that could ultimately cost people their lives, they were of the mindset that leadership was definitive.

The gathering of intel permitted all pertinent components to share facts and provide valuable input on determining a solution. The appointed leader would then determine the direction of appropriate action. Here it was, a participatory process that was ineffective and conflict oriented. Often leadership was determined by ownership of possessions, wealth, and exhibitions of emotions and passions. In Kate and Harry's viewpoint, this guaranteed one important outcome, the absence of "peace."

Every individual that entered the fray not only brought their commitment, energy, ideas, and resolve to eradicate slavery but their own "twist." That inalienable desire to say, "I was there too!" Something that would make you feel that you helped in resolving a hideous condition like slavery, but here's a little something to personally remember me by.

Just getting the job done wasn't enough now; it was necessary to carve your name in a tree to say that "you and your idea were here!" You and your noble idea took on a level of importance, even if it eventually killed the tree, or you add a handful of peppercorns into the cake batter just because you have a handful of peppercorns. This type of internal confusion occurs when one was neither familiar with nor made a commitment to learning and taking in the view from "both sides of the coin."

In the Finger Lakes Region of the state of New York, Harry and Kate Freeman did not have that problem. Everyone of concern knew where they came from, what they had done, and what they were doing. There was no greater authority on Africans in Africa, Africans in the New World, Africans in the colonies and African Americans in the United States of America than Harry and Kate Freeman. So, when the discussion of returning emancipated slaves and freeborn African Americans to Africa, it became a "twist" in the Underground Railroad Movement. The Finger Lakes Region of the state of New York, particularly the Auburn area, had the clarity it needed to reject that "twist," based wholeheartedly on the actual expertise and panoramic view of the Freemans.

Kate and Luke had explained to those "who needed to know," because Harry couldn't be so bothered because it interfered with his work. "The demarcation lines delineated on a map of Africa are arbitrary. They served the colonial interest of European nations and were the same nonsense they encountered in England. These arbitrary lines create great turmoil between Tribes and Clans within Tribes."

She further elaborated, "You cannot carve out a section of Africa where they are not exporting slaves and deposit emancipated Americanized slaves with limited to no knowledge of Africa, of different ethnic groups to compete and blend in with the people inhabiting that land is asking for continuous strife and conflict."

Explaining the issue of relocation to include "both sides of the coin" ended any further conversation in the Auburn area of relocating emancipated Americanized slaves to Africa. Unfortunately, the "Twist" of returning Americanized Blacks to Africa grew legs and avoided the death it so rightly deserved.

One day Daniel "Big Man" Hughes brought a visitor to see Kate and Harry at New Guinea. Before they could greet their guest, Kate had to remind Harry how he was supposed to respond to this guest at his home. Harry had no problems with guests anywhere on his property of New Guinea, but in his home was another issue. Guests at his home were people he cared about, not strangers appearing spontaneously. After being reminded about expectant behavior from his wife, Harry led Kate into the parlor to greet their guest and hug their bonus son.

Standing in the parlor was Mr. John Brown Russwurm. Mr. Russwurm was a very imposing figure with his erudite and exclamatory presentation of himself which immediately placed Kate and Harry on guard.

Harry had mentally moved into his attack dog mode and was just waiting for Kate to provide her tacit permission, but none came, so he was forced to stay at attention and attempt to be responsive to their "guest."

John Russwurm had impeccable credentials. He was the first African American to graduate from Bowdoin College in Maine. Mr. Russwurm and his partner had started the first African American newspaper in the United States called the *Freedom Journal*. Given all these notable accomplishments, Harry would have loved to have explored them with him over a good meal and a walk around New Guinea, but Mr. Russwurm was on a mission that would not permit him to dilly dally at New Guinea too long.

Mr. Russwurm was on a recruiting mission. He was well aware of the role that New Guinea played in the Underground Railroad Movement. He was also cognizant of the fact a good portion of runaway slaves from Maryland, Delaware, District of Columbia, and Virginia came through New Guinea. He was here to solicit the Freemans' support and guidance to recruiting African Americans and runaway slaves to return to Africa.

Kate guided Harry to his favorite chair in the parlor, which was a signal to Harry that he would hear Mr. Russwurm out before he was dismissed, then she turned to Mr. Russwurm and offered him some tea and a slice of pie which he gladly accepted. Big Man was already in the kitchen eating everything he could put his hands on and reminiscing with Platt and Luke because being at the Freemans was like being at home. This was one meeting where Luke and Platt did not need to be engaged in. They already knew the family decision once the announcement of Mr. Russwurm's affiliations were made clear.

During a brief round of chitchat, Mr. Russwurm was probing into Harry and Kate's history. He was interested in how they were able to survive economically amid a hostile environment of racial attitudes. He leaned forward and asked with all the sincerity he could muster, "What was making New Guinea so successful in aiding escaped slaves and freeborn African Americans in making a life here in Auburn and in Canada?"

Harry leaned forward in his chair and said, "God." Mr. Russwurm, startled by the simplicity of Harry's remark, sat back and got to the purpose of his visit.

Mr. Russwurm told Harry and Kate that he was an important member of the American Colonization Society (ACS) and that their goal was to provide safe passage and a safe habitat in Africa for African Americans. They had carved out a piece of land previously occupied by the Temne People in Africa and were starting a new country based on the principals of the United States for free and escape slaves of African American blood called Liberia. He furthered elaborated that the American Colonization Society of Maryland had sanctioned him to move forward with this innovative concept. He was leaving shortly for Africa to initiate The Republic of Maryland in Africa and that he would be the first governor of the Republic.

Harry looked at Kate, and they blurted out at the same time, "Chief Apunda."

Russwurm, looking dazed at these rustic Blacks appearing to have some familiarity with his modus operandi, asked, "Chief Apunda?"

Harry sat up in his chair with Kate holding his arm and with all the authority experience had bestowed upon him said, "Yes. Chief Apunda the Gbana, that's Noble to you, of the Temne People of the Kingdom of Koya that was north of Kate's Clan the Bubi People and my clan, the Beti-Pahuin People."

Raising his wife and himself from their chairs Harry said, "Let me introduce you to Rehema and Masego who Apunda captured and enslaved and our daughter Chipo whom they killed."

Mr. Russwurm, who was startled by the Freemans' revelations, stumbled with his verbiage for maybe the first time in his life and said, "I... I had no idea! I'm sorry if I opened old wounds and feelings!"

Kate stepped forward with a warming smile and said, "Mr. Russwurm, God has healed all wounds and feelings related to what happened to us and what was done to our child. Our concern is addressing the plan that you have shared with us."

Harry tagged in, "Mr. Russwurm, the Kingdom of Koya was the British biggest slave trading partner. There are also at least thirty different ethnic groups and clans who are not going to accept nor tolerate your Western culture approach to life smothering their way of life, politics, and customs. You and the people journeying with you will be seen as interlopers. Your reception will not be warm; there will be overt and covert opposition to your attempt to guide and dominate. The most distressing outcome will be that peace will always allude you, and you will have to learn to sleep with one eye opened. Those native Africans will not allow you to transform them into 'Darkies'!"

Mr. Russwurm had just been introduced to the well-known Freeman approach to message sent, message received, message understood, in other words, their "shock and awe" presentation! As he collected his posture and gathered his thoughts, he sheepishly uttered, "We've studied this thoroughly, and it has to work. We've put too much time, money, and effort into making The Republic of Maryland in Africa work! Mr. Freeman, times have changed greatly since you called it home. I really think it's time for a venture like the one we are putting forth! I would really like for you and Mrs. Freeman to weigh the good that could come out of relocating African Americans to Africa!"

Harry just sunk his head and Kate responded, "Mr. Russwurm, we see no value for African Americans or Africans of a mass migration of people whose skin happens to be some hue of color but have no cultural understanding. Our position is firm today, and it will be firm tomorrow; we will not be able to help you or support you in this endeavor. It also would not be wise for you to promulgate your vision in this area because people both black and white will send you right back here to New Guinea!" Parting proclamations were made, and Luke and Platt accompanied Big Man and Mr. Russwurm back down the hill.

Luke always found it amazing that the folks in the metropolitan coastal communities like Philadelphia, New York, and Boston considered themselves the prima facia authorities on all issues of importance to the movement. Their approach to intellectual dominance was driving an artificial crack into the Underground Railroad Movement. Regardless of these operational cracks and schisms, the Movement would always prosper because of the severity of the greatest problem the United States will ever face, slavery and its spiritual source of strength, racism.

The reality was that Upstate New York was as different from New York City as noon was different than midnight. The Vigilant Committees, which were extremely strong in Philadelphia, Boston, and New York City, were violent groups of militant abolitionists. Their focus was myopically focused on "An Eye for an Eye." Their rage had caused some members of the committees on the east coast to turn from defensive actions of protection for runaways and freeborn African Americans to taking offensive action against slave catchers' sympathizers and supporters of slavery. This was bringing too much attention to the work of the Underground Railroad and caused some people, who would be supporters to the cause to shy away from involvement because of the violence.

David Ruggles was a very violent crusader for the Underground Railroad Movement cause. He was continuously trying to convince Kate and Luke that a Vigilant Committee needed to be developed in Auburn. At a conference in New York City he cornered Luke for over an hour trying to convince him of the benefits of a Vigilant Committee of both White and Black participants. Luke would repeatedly tell him that the system employed at New Guinea worked well and brought no undue attention to their work for the freeing of slaves.

David thought a trip to Auburn to meet with Harry and Kate could gain favor. He quickly learned that he was badly mistaken. After some lemonade and two slice of Kate's rhubarb pie Harry, Kate, David, Platt, and Luke moved into the parlor. Luke and Platt brought up the rear smirking and sending eye messages that said, "This boy is about to catch total hell!"

Harry opened the conversation, "So, son, you are one of the leaders of the Vigilant Committee in New York City?"

David responded proudly, "Yes, sir, we handle our business!"

Harry responded, "Hmm, so you handle your business, and I suppose you get things done?"

"Yes, sir, we sure do! We make sure our message is clearly understood," quipped David.

"Son, let's take a walk; we'll be back shortly. I want to show you a little of New Guinea."

As David and Harry walked out the door Luke and Platt burst out in laughter. Platt turned to his mother who was giggling to herself and said, "He sure is. He's got fourteen Leopards stalking every step they take and ten Watch Women in support rolls with blow darts. This should be quite an awakening for Mr. Ruggles."

As Harry and David walked through New Guinea, Harry shared his and Kate's history and the role of New Guinea in the Underground Railroad Movement. Harry explained some very important aspects of a defensive military unit that reverts to an offensive posture when required. David looked befuddled and was trying to figure out why this old man was so passive. He had heard the legend of New Guinea and the Freemans. This was not what he expected.

Harry continued to explain to the young man that a good defensive military unit does not create conflicts or bring attention that much later could become a liability to our overall goals. Harry was taking him to the stumps behind the praise house in order to show him where strategy was developed with the guidance of the Lord.

David felt confident enough to bristle at Harry's words and demeanor, "If we don't take an active stance against these racists trying to subjugate all blacks, there will be no future for us or our children. You've got to fight fire with fire. You've got to let them know that I'm not taking it anymore!"

Harry turned to him and asked, "And where is that in the Bible?"

"What's the Bible got to do with this?" retorted David

"Everything, young man, everything. You remember the race riots in your own hometown New York City? Don't you realize that your heavy-handed response and approach contributed to making insecure individuals perfect candidates to go to work for the devil? David, you are trying to change people's minds. I work at changing people's hearts," Harry said with great sincerity.

Harry continued, "You can accomplish your necessary goals without the fanfare and notoriety your Vigilant Committees generate. I'm going to show you how we address a threat. Take a seat on the stump next to me."

As soon as David sat on the stump behind the praise house, he felt pressure on his neck and thigh. Startled, he saw two men each holding a stick, one at his throat area and the other in his upper thigh region. David had no idea that any other human being was even close to him or Harry, but when Harry told him to turn and look, there were twelve men with all sorts of weapons standing within ten feet from him.

Harry said, "Meet some of New Guinea's Tree Leopards. If you had been a real threat to the peace of New Guinea, those would have been knives instead of sticks. Now stroll over to bank of the outlet."

David started strolling towards the edge of the bank of the Owasco Outlet, running swiftly below his position, when he jumped back once again startled. There were four women camouflaged in the brush next to the bank's bush. Each woman had a blowgun aimed at him.

Harry had strolled up behind David and put his arm around David and said, "Kate wanted me to say hi and introduce you to the Watch Women. These four were ready to neutralize a threat with a poison that would stop a heart in thirty heartbeats. You also had the pleasure of meeting six other camouflaged Watch Women on our walk over; I'll show you where they are hidden in plain sight. Mr. Ruggles, we take our freedom very seriously."

"David," Harry said gaining the young man's full attention, "we neither fault nor taunt others with what the Lord has given us. We witness every day the meanness of racism and slavery, but Kate and I learned a long time ago that as long as we stay obedient to the Will of God all we have to do is endure and be prepared to achieve what God has for us to accomplish."

"Mr. Freeman, are you trying to tell me that we are supposed to be submissive to the wrongs these white folks are perpetrating on us? We just supposed to sing our little "Swing Lo Sweet Chariot" songs and kowtow to their whims and farces? I ain't no sheep waiting to be slaughtered!" It was as if David was expelling through his verbiage years of hate and confusion. As if this old Black man had gained the balance he so desired but in a way that was completely unorthodox to the world they lived in.

"Son, I'm not telling you to do anything or be any-thing thing that this world tries to label you as or make you be. I'm trying to tell you to let God guide your every step. David, do you know what a guinea sack is?"

Sure, you're talking about those burlap bags. We use them all the time to package stuff and carry stuff around," replied the stunned young man. What the hell does a burlap bag or guinea sack have to do with our conversation? He thought to himself.

"You ever thought how they got their name and what those burlap bags were used for?" Harry asked.

"No, not really never gave it any thought," was David's reply.

"Well, for you it is just a convenient tool to be used at your convenience. Mr. Ruggles, they got their name because of their use. In my home country of Guinea, they were burlap bags that were used by white people to place our captured infants in at the time of enslavement. This was done for easy transport and disposal of the infants if necessary, but it also had a major psychological effect upon us."

"Our resistance to capture, movement, and submission was hindered and abated by our concern for our most precious possessions, our babies. Mr. Ruggles, you don't know hatred until you see your child being mistreated and harmed and crying out to you and you can't do a thing about it. Listening to her screams and cries day and night and then learning they killed and burned your baby in that burlap bag they call a guinea sack while they were raping your wife takes you to a level of hate that you cannot recover from without turning to God."

"Sir," David interrupted with a level of compassion he had never realized before, "it sounds quite personal to you."

"It is David. Mrs. Freeman's and my oldest child Chipo was killed by Clear People, that's what we called white people, in that manner in Africa. If it wasn't for God's intervention and direction, we would not be having this philosophical discussion. So, the reality of the situation is every guinea sack, burlap bag, we see is a reminder to what was done to our daughter, but by being obedient to God's Will for our lives, the sting of hurt and hatred are gone. Nothing in this world or made by man could have done that, only God."

Looking deep into Ruggles's eyes Harry said, "Might does not make right. God does!"

They returned to the Freeman homestead in New Guinea with David beginning to have questionable doubt about his approach to supporting the Underground Railroad Movement. More intimate to his thought process was his motivation and intent for what he professed.

David remained active in components of the Movement while opening the first African American bookstore in the United States. David would attempt to get permission from Harry and Kate to tell their incredible story, but they would vehemently refuse, "If God wants someone to know, He'll tell them." David Ruggles major claim to fame would be his helping a young dynamic preacher named Frederick Douglas escape slavery.

Frederick had visited New Guinea and enjoyed sitting with Kate and Harry to learn firsthand what life was like in Africa and the actual process of enslavement and the emotional and spiritual toll it took on them, but what really stoked his interest was how they were able to reconcile their faith in God having been thrust into a lifestyle of grief and loss by men who claim to have faith in

God, Kate and Harry explained to him how God brought them out and the commitment they made to God for them, their children, and their children's children.

Frederick, Sojourner, and Big Man and many more were regular visitors to New Guinea where they could leave their prestige and fame at the doormat and just be family. Sitting at the feet of the inspiring wisdom of Kate and Harry Freeman that was given to them by God.

14

HANNIBAL FREEMAN

Ethel Freeman was not liking what she was seeing. Grandma Kate had given her the task of staying on top of all the Suffragette's business, but her little cousin Hannibal was providing her some angst. She would tell her dad that "Hannibal was happy with himself." When Harry Jr. would inquire into what she meant by that she responded, "He's in his own world. He's lost in his own thoughts. I just think he is too head strong."

"Well," said her dad, "the boy has had it rougher than most. With Uncle James dying early and his mother trying to make ends meet, he was pretty much raising himself in a room by himself; that don't help you to mingle and socialize with people. The best thing that has happened for that boy was Aunt Sally moving back to New Guinea and reuniting with her daughter Caroline. Even though Caroline got married to that De Puy boy, she works hard at schooling our youngsters here, and Platt said he wouldn't be able to do what he does here at New Guinea if it wasn't for her husband John De Puy. Everybody is praying for Hannibal, and I'll be working with him once he gets a little older."

"Okay, Dad, I just had him on my mind. I wish I had more time to spend with him, but I've got to get ready for Sojourner. She's coming tomorrow, and we are going to be really busy."

"Oh, Bell, I mean, Sojourner is coming tomorrow?" Harry Jr. said excitedly. "It's the only time I see you lighten up a little bit. You and she have always been close, and I just enjoy sitting back and watching you play and laugh. Please give her my love and tell her I'm sorry I missed her. I must be gone the next three or four days taking care of family business in Geneva, Pen Yan, and Lyons."

"Knowing Sojourner, I think she may be gone before I get back," Harry Jr. said with a chuckle.

"You're right, Dad. She's going to spend the night, then her and I head for Seneca Falls, Waterloo, and Rochester. After Rochester, I head back home, and Sojourner heads to St. Catharine, Canada, to meet with William Merritt. Then she ventures to Africa, Ohio, for a meeting with the Wesleyan church people."

Ethel paused and shook her head and said, "Too much traveling for me! She wanted me to go with her, but I'm not built to travel like that! That's too much traveling for me! She truly lives up to her name, 'So-journer,' the traveler spreading the 'Truth,'" she said with a chuckle.

Sojourner Truth loved the Freemans. They had been a ray of hope for her while she was enslaved. Harry and Kate had been guiding lights spiritually, emotionally, and in this world of racial hatred, she consider Ethel as a sister. Sojourner never missed an opportunity to visit the Freemans at New Guinea in Auburn. Ethel and Sojourner were contemporaries and had developed a bond that only two precocious and extremely serious young ladies could with their encounters in New Guinea and Rifton, New York, in Ulster County growing up.

Back then it was Bell and Ethel, the no nonsense twins, one free and one enslaved. Bell had gained her freedom and shed off her slave name and became Sojourner Truth. Now, at every opportunity related to the growth of the Suffragette Movement or the Underground Railroad Movement, Sojourner invited Ethel to represent the Freemans of Auburn, New York.

Meanwhile, Mary Freeman was developing a greater relationship with Fanny Seward. Yes, decorating the Seward Mansion and discussing and creating clothing designs for women in Fanny's circle was enough motivation for Mary to venture down the hill, but Fanny's real passion was the vast network of safehouses she and Mary were developing in Auburn and Cayuga County.

The supporters of slavery, slave catchers, and sympathizers of controlling and removing blacks in their environ had realized the pattern of safehouses. Slave owners had created a cottage industry that specialized in counter espionage as it related to the Underground Railroad Movement. They knew that safehouses were:

- Homes of people with deep spiritual beliefs which rendered slavery unacceptable.
- Reputable members of their community.
- Predominantly White.
- People who did not live in little houses, three to five rooms etc.
- People who had something to lose if charged under the Fugitive Slave Laws.

This counter intelligent unit for slavers did not travel in packs with hound dogs. They maneuvered individually, masquerading as providers of utensils or services reconnoitering hot beds of anti-slavery activities. It was not beneath them to masquerade as an abolitionist in order to gain insight into the workings of the Underground Railroad Movement in that community. It had been intimated that these individuals were quite active in creating unrest between blacks and newly arriving immigrants competing for the same jobs.

The Freemans, having seen the race riots and unrest along the eastern seaboard and out west in Cincinnati, needed no other alert to move into a preparatory mode. Kate and Harry had taught their children to turn every mole hill into a mountain; that way you were prepared for any challenge it may present. They also instilled the belief that the best way to kill a flea is with an axe; take nothing for granted.

Because of Mary and Luke's frequent and lengthy visits to the Seward home, along with Platt's providing servants and workers to the estate, it would be extremely difficult for anyone to see behavior out of the ordinary that would divulge the arrival of runaway slaves.

All operations conducted by the Freemans and the community of New Guinea were operating smoothly. Harry and Kate's dream of having an AME Zion church in Auburn had grown into a flourishing start. All was well in the world for the Freemans. Their children were running all the enterprises, but there was something amiss in the Freeman household.

Hannibal Freeman was a different child. During his early formative years, he had not been involved with his Freeman relatives, but the family had been working hard to develop the traditional family traditions and ways. He and his mother had resettled in New Guinea after his father James's death. It was clear that the isolation of his first few years of life had turned him inward in thought and emotion.

Hannibal's father James had decided to pursue his comfort and fortune away from the Freeman Homestead in New Guinea just like his brother Sidney and his sister Jane. James was determined to answer to no one in setting the course of his life. His pursuit of the good life and the freedom of doing what he wanted to do when he wanted to do it led James to sell himself into slavery.

Coming to his senses in 1815 he repurchased his freedom and was working in the Albany, New York, area and trying to reestablish his marriage with Sally. His pride would not allow him to pack his family up and return to New Guinea, even though many overtures were made by his parents and siblings. Tragedy struck without notice; James had an accident at work and died. The death of James caused Harry and Kate along with their son Harry Jr. to go get Sally and the young Hannibal and bring them home to New Guinea to be reunited with her older daughter and the rest of the family.

Grandma and Grampa Freeman doted on the young Hannibal and eventually got him to smile and laugh for the first time. Uncle Harry took him under his wing as the boy child he never had. Everyone was working hard to help with his adjustment to this caring family.

Uncle Harry was given a task that would cause him great consternation. Hannibal would not take to his schooling. Nothing that was done to him would cause him to conform to sitting in a room and learning. He would escape and get caught playing on the cliffs of the Owasco Outlet or playing in a tree or wandering in some remote spot of the Auburn area. Harry had decided that placing Hannibal in a working environment might be the solution.

To Harry Jr. and the family's chagrin, settling Hannibal Freeman into a traditional pattern of behavior would prove contrary to Hannibal's nature. Not being allowed to venture into educational and social ventures white children were afforded made very few options for a child of Hannibal's nature. Hannibal was also trying to cope with a forced name change. White folks found it easier to tolerate William better than Hannibal. So, around Auburn he was known as William. It was thought the new name would allow him to dissipate the historical fear that white folks had in the name Hannibal, who appeared to not stay in his place assigned by white folks.

Hannibal "William" Freeman was destined to collide with society given his singular purpose of self, the unfairness of race relationships among God's people, and the greed and hatred producing climates of fear and retribution in our nation.

Black people were considered a lunatic, insane, or crazy if they "didn't stay in their place" as defined by white folks. Exhibiting any normal traits portrayed by white children were considered "eccentricities." Being reserved in speech and not revealing complete exposure to your thoughts or intentions would cause a Black person to be labeled with "taciturnity." That is being reserved in speech, not volunteering anything more than necessary talk. Hannibal "William" Freeman had not learned "the game" as taught by Harry and Kate to diffuse White folks unfounded anxieties, and it was not in his nature to learn.

Hannibal had the adventurous spirit of his grand-father Harry. He liked to rove and discover. Uncle Platt had placed him in several positions in and around the Auburn area, but he always ended up being fired for not staying on task or playing with his friends. When Hannibal was about ten years old, Uncle Harry thought that maybe a change of venue would help with Hanni-bal's development. Harry contacted Judge Satterlee of Lyons, New York, in Wayne County about a position for Hannibal. Wayne County had not taken on the growth boom that Cayuga County had over the last thirty years. It still had traces of the wilderness and could possibly provide Hannibal with an environment more suitable to his nature.

Unfortunately, that didn't work out. Uncle Luke put him to work in his barbershop as a shoe black. When Luke would look for him to clean and polish a pair of boots, Hannibal was nowhere to be found. Hannibal Freeman refused to be confined in a kitchen, building, or yard. To punish him for such behavior just made him more recalcitrant, but he had good sense not to cross the line of Freeman disobedience that could cause his elders to administer a punishment that he may not be able to recover from.

As Hannibal grew older, family concerns related to Hannibal grew also. The constable had come to New Guinea looking for Hannibal. He said he needed to talk to William about a horse being stolen in Sennett. Platt informed the constable that he would bring William to his office as soon as he could be located.

When William came in for the evening meal that his sister had prepared, Platt asked him, "What do you know about a horse up in Sennett being stolen today?"

"Nothing!" William exclaimed. "I ain't been nowhere close to Sennett in days."

"Well, after dinner you and I have got to go see the constable and get this thing straightened out," Platt informed him.

After dinner, Platt and William headed on down the hill to the sheriff's office. It appears that a Martha Godfrey of Sennett had her horse stolen by a teenage Black boy, according to a witness, a Mr. Doty. Mr. Doty claimed that he saw a Black boy on that horse the evening it disappeared. When Martha Godfrey relayed the information that Mr. Doty had conveyed to her to the authorities, she told them that Jack Furman, a teenage Black boy, had been doing some work in the neighborhood.

The constable figured Furman was close enough to Freeman that he went to investigate William Freeman. William provided him an account of his whereabouts for the evening in question. Once the constable had gathered all pertinent information, William went before Judge Cook. Judge Cook reviewed the information presented to him. He found William's whereabouts substantiated. Judge Cook freed William and cleared him of all charges presented.

Jack Furman, a Black teenager, had been spending a great deal of time in the Weedsport-Sennett area doing some odd and end jobs. He had a minor run in with Harry Jr. when he had done some sloppy work claiming to be a part of the Freeman enterprise. That had been awhile back, and nothing had been heard from or about Jack Furman in recent memory.

It was about three weeks after the horse was stolen that it was discovered eighty miles away in Chemung County, and it was determined that Jack Furman had sold the horse. He was arrested and remanded to the county jail in Auburn. While in jail he learned that William Freeman had been originally charged and jailed for the theft. Jack began his campaign to clear himself of all charges by claiming William Freeman stole the horse.

Eventually his campaign of lies took root, and William Freeman was rearrested for the thievery of Martha Godfrey's horse. Neither all the protestation from William and his family nor the evidence that enunciated Freeman's innocence could dissuade the legal apparatus of the county from charging William Freeman with the charge of horse theft.

Luke had sought out the advice of an old friend, a gentleman who was governor of the state of New York and had returned home for some sort of big meeting and a proper haircut from his old friend Luke, Governor William Henry Seward.

Luke explained to the governor what was happening to William and his current predicament. The governor explained that, given the history of the case and William's whereabouts being confirmed, that he should be exonerated when the county judicial system moved to resolve this case. William Seward concluded with remorse, "Madame Justice can't find her blindfold when it comes to African Americans."

Hannibal "William" Freeman was terrified. He was locked up in the county jail for something he hadn't done. Jack Furman was also locked up in the county jail, continually promoting his innocence and Williams's guilt regardless of the evidence against him.

William's fear was that the truth wasn't going to matter. White folks had never applied the law or the processing of the law in the same manner for Blacks. Spending time at Auburn State Prison for a crime he didn't do gave him daymares and nightmares.

Auburn Prison was one of the oldest prisons in the country. The community of Auburn had been given the choice of being the state capitol or having a state prison. Auburn chose the state prison. Being the capitol of a state brought you prestige and notoriety, but having a prison brought you wealth. A continuous stream of free (really slave labor given the tag on to their sentences "hard labor") laborers that neither had an advocate nor a recourse to cruelty and inhumane treatment. The human grinder was no place for any human being, let alone an African American teenager in the year 1840 in the United States of America.

Auburn State Prison had achieved the distinction of being the top supplier of silkworms and silk fabric in the United States. All leading infrastructure projects had prison laborers working. Quarries in the area had more inmates working in them than non-inmates. Farms were prospering with convict labor.

Harry Freeman would say, "Since its opening in 1817, Auburn State Prison has been our largest business competitor. It's hard to compete with free enslaved laborers from the prison. Someday God's going to bring this entire madness to an end."

Hannibal "William" Freeman was not going to be enslaved in prison for a crime he didn't commit. So, he escaped from the county jail. Once escaping, he ran up the hill to New Guinea to safety. His escape was at night and had not been discovered yet by the jailer. Hannibal banged on Ethel Freeman's door and hollered, "Ethel, I'm scared!"

Hannibal found himself in front of his uncles, Harry, Luke and Platt. Ethel had gone and gotten them while Hannibal sat in her kitchen eating.

"How did you get out of jail in the middle of the night?" asked Harry Jr.

"I got away 'cause I'm not going to prison for something I didn't do!" Hannibal said. "I'll die if I'm placed in that hole!"

"Well, Hannibal, all we can do is pray for deliverance from God. Your running from the law is sure enough a way to get yourself killed," said Luke.

Platt walked slowly towards Hannibal and sat down and looked him deep in the eyes and said, "You wouldn't be in this mess if you had listened. Hurry up and finish eating; we're taking you back down the hill to jail."

Hannibal finished his meal. He and his uncles proceeded down the hill to jail. Platt, Luke, and Harry Jr. were hoping to get him back there before the jailer realized he was gone and had notified the sheriff. It was too late. The sheriff, the three constables, and a few men with dogs had already gathered. It was too late to avoid the escape charge.

Hannibal was reincarcerated and went to trial on charges of stealing a horse and escaping from jail. He was sentence to five years of "hard labor." Jack Furman, for his lies, was given his freedom. It wasn't long before Furman was caught stealing another horse and was arrested.

Hannibal would not conform to his situation in jail. He continuously proclaimed his innocence and refused to meld his personality with the deprivation prison guards attempted to heap on him. Hannibal found himself being constantly beaten and punished for five years. They beat the Hannibal Freeman out of him and produced what they wanted, William Freeman.

William never accepted his plight all the way through his five-year sentence and paid the price physically, emotionally, and spiritually. His conviction on the issue of the horse theft was totally unjust. He was never charged for the escape thanks to the intervention of his family and authorities realizing he should never had been rearrested.

Upon his release from prison in September 1845, William attempted to secure retribution through traditionally official venues. First, he went to the Magistrate Bostwick's office and requested that warrants be taken out on the people that lied about him stealing a horse. William was summarily dismissed and told not to return. He then proceeded to the sheriff's office and told him that the Auburn State Prison had robbed him of his wages. William informed the sheriff that he had received only $1.42 for five years of work. He wanted a just amount for working that hard for that long. Once again, he was told to vacate the office and do not return.

There had been very little interaction between the Freemans and the Van Nest family. William's reasoning and rationale for his assault on the Van Nest family on the evening of March 12, 1846 was unknown to William's family. William's killing and maiming was viewed as abhorrent to everything the Freeman Family had been taught about human decency and respect for human life.

The horrendous murders and crimes committed against the Van Nest Family and friends by William Freeman, the son of the late James and Sally Freeman, are well documented and discussed. The Freemans prayed for the souls of the Van Nest family murdered and their friends that were harmed in William's attack and for comfort from God for their loved ones and the community in general. The family also prayed that Hannibal would seek forgiveness from God for his actions; because they already knew trial or no trial, he was a dead man.

They had tried to lynch him early before his court trial, and the conditions he was kept in during and after the trial would assure Hannibal "William" Freeman's death. Platt would say later, "Three wrongs don't make a right. What they did to Hannibal about the horse. What Hannibal did to those people. What they did to Hannibal during and after the court trial. All of it was wrong and out of the Will of God. A perfect result of disaster based on man's free will; it only had one purpose: to stir up more fear and hatred."

15

THE EVOLUTION of CHANGE

Harry and Kate had always preached to their children and grandchildren, "My children, 'endure' in God until the 'Great I Am' changes the situation; then prepare to 'achieve' according to God's directions."

Harry and Kate had taken up their dancing positions around the throne of God. No longer would the Freeman Family seek out their earthly and spiritual wisdom in person. They would have to rely on the library of spiritual, emotional, and physical lessons they had shared over many decades of loving interactions.

Things were changing in the country, the Finger Lakes Region, and within the Freeman Family. Harry Jr. was spending more time in the western region increasing the number of runaway slaves moving through the Underground Railroad Movement from New Guinea to Rochester. Platt was now completely responsible for everything pertaining to the maintenance and operations of New

Guinea. Caroline and her husband Aaron Denum had moved from Fleming to Syracuse after William Freeman's trial. Luke had purchased a home across the street from the Sewards and a half a block from the Hardenberghs.

William Seward had exposed in the William Freeman trial the duplicity of the criminal court system towards African Americans. Seward's conviction to justice and humanity was quite apparent, even during a racially charged murder trial. Seward showed the nation that he took our founding beliefs very seriously. As governor, he advocated for prison reform in the early stages of our developing penal system by placing libraries in the state prisons.

Mr. Seward was the humanitarian's humanitarian. His philosophy was simple, "It is our mandate from God to show love and respect to all human beings." Seward had become quite interested in what the British courts were exploring with the issue of criminal insanity and had explored the issue as it related to the United States courts. The former governor saw a young man from a family that he and Fanny had a very close relationship with, the Freemans, who was in need of legal counsel and exhibiting signs of abnormal mental acuity.

Some members of the Freeman family did not care for a plea of insanity concerning Hannibal and believed that vile treatment by society and the hatred and mistreatment of African Americans had created this version of Frankenstein called William Freeman. He would not have been able to commit such killings and maimings without the inducement of a racist society. The elders of the family were well aware of that and had to remind those family members that were getting lost in the old testament, "an eye for and eye..." about the Freeman family history from Africa to Auburn. There was great compassion towards their opinions to the predicament Hannibal was immersed in, but they had been firmly instructed to maintain their silence, pray, and "let the governor do his work."

The original trial was a farce. Any Black witness for the defense was immediately discredited and was being held to a standard that White folks could not obtain. The trial ended with William Freeman found guilty of four counts of murder. The former governor William Seward was able to overturn the guilty verdict rendered by the Cayuga County court by securing a new trial for William through the New York State Supreme Court.

William Seward was unable to pursue justice for William because of the putrid conditions he was kept in while in the county jail. William Freeman would die in custody because of those conditions on August 21, 1847 awaiting a new trial. After his death, the autopsies confirmed major abnormalities in his brain thus lending credence to the plea of insanity in the United States court system. Hannibal "William" Freeman was never found legally guilty of the Van Nest murders. The William Freeman trial galvanized Americans stance on the issues of slavery and race relationships that would lead to the Compromise of 1850, The Fugitive Slave Act of 1850, the Dredd Scott Decision, The Missouri Compromise, the Civil War, Jim Crow, Segregation, Desegregation up till our current James Crow Era.

Most of the third generation of Freemans, the grandchildren, largely wanted to be independent and moved away from New Guinea. Harry Jr. had two children, Ethel Freeman and Daniel Freeman. Luke and Catherine had six children, Harriet Freeman, Helen Freeman, Lewis Freeman, Matilda Freeman, George Freeman, and Burgett Freeman. Platt and Mary also had six children, Fanny Freeman, Charles Freeman, John Freeman, Jackson Freeman, Thomas Freeman, and William "J" Roundtree Freeman. Most of these children would cast their lots and seek their fortunes in places like Cleveland; New Orleans; St. Catharine, Canada; Philadelphia; and other places that seemed exotic and faraway from what was familiar to them, New Guinea and Auburn, New York.

Luke, Catherine, Platt, and Mary were left with the task of maintaining New Guinea and the Freeman enterprises and their involvement in the Underground Railroad Movement. Luke's popularity and notoriety as a barber and advocate of pertinent issues of the day had folks saying around town, "If he wasn't Black, he could be the next governor of the state of New York." To those who were exposed to his compassion and concern for all people of all colors could be heard quipping, "I don't care what anybody say; Mr. Luke Freeman was as good as any White man."

Luke was barbering in his own building and traveling and strategizing on issues related to the Underground Railroad Movement. Catherine had closed the gun repair shop and was helping with the maintenance of New Guinea's as best she could from the bottom of the hill, in her new home, while raising her children. Mary was still sewing but was putting her time in with Fanny Seward with the wellbeing and operations of the safe houses while raising her children. Platt was the backbone of New Guinea and was keeping it viable for African Americans who had decided to settle in the Auburn area and maintaining its role in the Underground Railroad Movement. Platt had committed himself to his father's goal for New Guinea, but he built a home on a part of the land the family owned on Cornel Street about a half mile southwest of New Guinea.

Luke was becoming an artful mediator in Underground Railroad human friction. Two of the movements most important journalists, the publishers of the *North Star* and *Liberator*, book writers, orators, and spokesmen were at odds over style and approach. Frederick Douglas and William Lloyd Garrison good friends, who were totally committed to the abolitionist movement had disagreements amongst themselves that had created a division within the Underground Railroad Movement.

With the Compromise of 1850 and the subsequent Fugitive Slave Act enacted that fall, the relative safety that the big urban centers on the east coast, Philadelphia, New York, and Boston had provided was under attack by slave catchers with the support of local law enforcement agencies. Conductors on the Underground Railroad were finding it more and more difficult to find safety in those communities causing them to take advantage of Big Man's Susquehanna River Line on the Underground Railroad.

Daniel "Big Man" Hughes ran a barge the entire length of the Susquehanna River, and Harry Jr.'s son Daniel Freeman was a key part of his operations north of Elmira. The Susquehanna River ran for four hundred and fifty miles with twists and turns and rapids that no ship had ever been able to navigate. These natural obstacles gave Big Man a monopoly for transporting lumber and supplies on his barge between his home in Williamsport, Pennsylvania, and Havre de Grace, Maryland, just north of Baltimore. This watery trek through frontier America was also perfect for the movement of runaway slaves.

One conductor on the Underground Railroad that Big Man had brought to New Guinea was a no-nonsense, extremely serious, and spiritual young lady named Harriet Tubman. Harriet herself was a runaway. Harriet was on a mission from the Lord and liked the idea of Black folks having a homestead and caring for one another right here in the United States. There were no frantic worries about police showing up with a slave catcher and harassing the people living in New Guinea. This was her kind of place. The more she talked with the Freemans and played with the small children like William Roundtree, Platt's son, the more she felt that Auburn could be a perfect place for her and her family. Mary had already introduced Harriet to Fanny Seward and other participants in their safehouse network like Amelia Bloomer, Elizabeth Cady Stanton, Martha Coffin Wright, Lucretia Mott, and Susan B Anthony, but now Mary needed personal intervention on behalf of Harriet. There was only one person to see and that would be the senator's wife Frances Seward.

Mary and Harriet ventured down the hill and met with Fanny Seward about Harriet Tubman wanting to relocate to Auburn. Fanny was delighted to hear that Harriet wanted to be a part of what they were doing in Auburn on a permanent basis. She told them that she would discuss it with William and see how they could assist. Harriet and Mary were delighted with their meeting with Fanny and went skipping back up the hill. They were full of hope that Harriet would be able to call Auburn home. Returning to Mary's house, they sat in the kitchen eating a slice of Mary's rhubarb pie (Mary had learned her mother-in-law's recipe), giving all praise to God for the wonders that were working in their lives.

Harriet took a walkthrough New Guinea towards the stumps behind the old Praise House. She had learned from her previous visits with the Freemans that this was a strong place to commune with God. She saw Platt's son, William Roundtree, who was now a young teenager, and convinced him to come with her. Harriet was William's hero. The young man was in awe of Harriet's exploits and constant exposure to danger with everything dependent on the guidance of the Lord. He had made up his mind that he wanted that kind of relationship with God and to make the same kind of impact in the world. William, too, had a lot to pray for because soon he would need his parents' permission to make his dream take root.

He was enjoying his work with the senator and friend of the family William Seward. Being a footman for Senator William Seward was exposing him to people, places, and topics that were not available to the average teenager and absolutely were not in the purview of a Black teenager. Young Roundtree couldn't wait until his necessary public schooling was completed and his parents gave him permission to work full time for the senator, even when he was in Washington, DC.

Harriet and William reached the stumps and began to praise and worship God for being God all by Himself. He did not need any human being or human action to make things possible. They both enjoyed the tranquility this time in this place brought them.

When they had finished worshipping God, Harriet told William, "All this notoriety and attention that people try to heap on me don't phase me at all. William, I don't want to be no famous speaker or headliner at some big convention; all I want is my family and to be able to live in peace and help whoever God sends my way."

At dinner that evening, Harriet and Mary told Platt, Luke, Catherine, Ethel, Daniel Freeman who was in town picking up supplies for his dad Harry Jr., and Big Man what had transpired at the meeting with Fanny Seward. Everyone was excited for Harriet with Luke providing a note of caution, "Knowing William Seward as I do, he will come up with a viable plan to make this happen. My concern is that our country is building walls around issues that are going to make corrective dialogue useless and lead to armed conflict. Besides, Douglass and Garrison are spending more time bickering over philosophical haranguing about paying for your freedom and the constitution that I'm afraid it's impacting the movement."

Luke stood up looked at everyone in the room and said, "I think it would be in our best interest not to share this information about Harriet with anyone at this time. We should wait until the Sewards reveal their plan and it is consummated."

Everyone in the room agreed, and no more talk was had until the papers were signed declaring that Harriet Tubman was now an official resident of Auburn, New York.

16

A PROOF OF MANHOOD

Harriet Tubman had completed her land acquisition from the Sewards and now was a permanent resident of Auburn, New York. Harriet was enjoying having a home for herself and her family but knew peace was going to be delayed. She knew that war clouds were on the horizon with the election of Abraham Lincoln as president of the United States. Her commitment to her mission for God of freeing slaves and her desire to assure freedom for members of her family made it clear that she would have to fight until the slave issue in the United States of America was finally eliminated.

"God sure does work in mysterious ways," as Platt told the Freeman Family and fellow church members as they gathered for the traditional Freemans' Thanksgiving Spiritual Service and Feast. Normally Luke would have this task of addressing the family and the members of the local AME Zion church that gathered with the Freemans on this occasion every year, but Luke had taken ill, and now it was time for Platt to assume the responsibilities.

"Man may see things one way, but it doesn't matter. The only thing that matters is believing that God has a solution to whatever may be the problem. The ill will of slavery has permeated this land that we call home since before we became a sovereign nation. Its tentacles of hatred, depredation, and servitude sought to destroy our parents Harry and Kate, but God said otherwise and allowed them to prosper in spite of the tentacles of slavery."

Platt paused and took a sip of his lemonade and said, "It looks like the Lord has used a pebble in David's slingshot to impact this goliath of slavery. Neither uprisings nor revolts could shake the footing of slavery in America, but God shaped a small, smooth stone in the image of a black slave that didn't have long to live named Dred Scott, and that old slue-footed goliath called slavery showed how vulnerable it had become. It has now been exposed as the spirit consuming evil that it is, growing more and more vulnerable to being obliterated because of the request of good God-fearing people. It's hard to worship God and deny another human being their God-given rights. It is easier to take up arms and rid ourselves of this abomination. John Brown did. Now we shall have to also. With the election of Abraham Lincoln to be the next president of these United States, talking is over. As the Bible says, 'Choose ye this day...' or as the old folks would say, 'Is you is, or is you ain't...' The choice is ours. It's time to prove to this state of New York, to this country called the United States of America, and to this world that God has given to us that we are men given the right to be men by God!"

People were amazed at how well Platt had spoken. Everyone knew that Luke had been the orator in the family, but Luke had had a stroke and was only able to sit there with an agreeing nod and a hearty thump on the table with his good hand. Luke's illness had made his and Platt's bonds even tighter. Now, Platt would have to lead the family in all matters, but he had able assistance with his with Mary and their son William J. Roundtree Freeman.

William had latched on to his father the same way Platt had latched on to Harry. William wanted to learn everything he could. William had sat up under Big Man and Harriet to listen to and learn about the intrigue and harrowing tales of conducting on the Underground Railroad. He had sat on the stumps behind the praise house and listened to his dad and his Uncle Luke discuss and resolve issues and concerns related to the Underground Railroad Movement. William would be sitting in the kitchen when his mom would be talking to Aunt Catherine about safehouses and types of clothing needed for the recently freed runaway slaves. He was amazed to learn that the center of the nation's Suffragette Movement was in the tiny Waterloo/Seneca Falls area; he thought that such an important and large movement would have had a New York City or Boston etc. as it center. He was particularly amazed by the people who would seek council from his uncle, his mom and his dad like, William Still, Sojourner Truth, Frederick Douglas, and others.

William was a sponge soaking up all the knowledge he had available to him, but being a sponge could not handle what he had become exposed to recently. His parents had given him permission to work full time for Senator William H. Seward. Senator William Seward was heading to the inauguration of the sixteenth president of the United States, Abraham Lincoln, and accompanying him was William Roundtree Freeman, his coachman.

The president-elect Abraham Lincoln had offered Senator Seward a position in his cabinet. Mr. Lincoln had asked Mr. Seward to become the Secretary of State for the United States of America. Initially this invitation surprised the Senator, but once he thought about the offer, he saw it as a brilliant strategy. William Seward had great foresight and could see that Lincoln was surrounding himself with the best talents given the upcoming problems the nation would be facing.

Lincoln and Seward had been rivals for the Republican nomination for president of the United States. They both had proven their oratory and leadership skills in the Senate and elsewhere after the Dred Scott Decision. Going into the convention, Senator Seward was the frontrunner for the nomination but was unable to secure the necessary votes on the first ballot. On the third ballot Senator Lincoln was able to secure the necessary votes to be the Republican Party's nominee for president. That fall, Senator Abraham Lincoln of Illinois was elected the sixteenth president of the Unites States of America.

Lincoln knew he needed a secretary of state that could be as efficient and effective as Benjamin Franklin had been for the country during the Revolutionary War. That man, in Lincoln's eyes, was William Seward. Lincoln knew that if war came, even though Lincoln was prepared to do whatever was necessary to keep the union together including maintaining slavery, he would need Seward's diplomatic skills to keep foreign entities out of the fray. Now, after taking the oath as the sixteenth president of the United States, it would be time for Lincoln and Seward to get busy saving the Union, and William Freeman was right there with them.

The most important state in the secessionist plans was Virginia, but the loudest was South Carolina, and before President Lincoln could settle into the White

House, South Carolina made sure that the issue of slavery would be decided by guns and death.

The call went out for men to take up arms and "save the Union," but once again, fear kept the government of the United States of America from allowing Black men to prove their worthiness in battle. To prove that these values that the United States of America attested to were worth fighting for and dying if necessary to affirm.

Frederick Douglas seized on the moment to expound on the Black man's right to prove himself and took his challenge to politicians in Washington and throughout the Union. Eventually, with their increasing loses, the government and Union Army relented and authorized the creation of regiments of colored troops. The United States War Department General Order number 143 issued on May 22, 1863 created the Bureau of Color Troops, establishing 175 regiments of Color Troops. The United States Color Troops (USCT) was composed primarily of African Americans but also included Native Americans, Hispanic Americans, Pacific Islanders, and Asian Americans.

> *"Without the Military help of the black freedmen, the war against the south could not have been won."*
>
> *President Abraham Lincoln, 1865*

Harriet Tubman and other freed African Americans and enslaved African Americans didn't need a "General Order" or permission to commence their spying activities for the Union. William Jackson, who was a house servant and personal coachman to Confederate President Jefferson Davis, provided essential detailed information about confederate logistics and strategies. Robert Smalls not only provided important information about confederate naval operations, but he also commandeered a confederate naval ship. Hundreds of slaves and free Blacks provided the Union a trove of pertinent information obtained by spying during the Civil War. Harriet was requested by the war department to lead expeditions of infantry into the deep South. She completed those expeditions several times with successful conclusions and continued to lead slaves to freedom. This was extremely important to the Union's war efforts because Harriet and other conductors were helping to deplete the slave workforce that was forced to support the Confederate States' war efforts.

General Order number 143 issued by the United States of America's War Department was viewed as the "Great Opportunity" by African Americans. Frederick Douglas's sons fought for the Union and were some of the first African Americans to enlist. Lewis Douglas was the drill sergeant for the 54th Massachusetts Volunteers CT. The "cry to arms" ranged through the valleys and hills of upstate New York and echoed through the blood of Harry and Kate's children. Every able-bodied grandson of Harry and Kate Freeman enlisted to fight for country and their futures, and fight they did.

Charles Freeman, John Freeman, William Freeman, Jackson Freeman, Thomas Freeman, Daniel Freeman, Lewis Freeman, George Freeman, and Burgett Freeman all enlisted into the United States of America's Color Troops. They fought in the 39th Reg USCT, the 11th Heavy Artillery USCT, the 22nd Reg USCT, the 31st Reg USCT, the 10th Reg USCT.

The siege of St. Petersburg, the battle for Richmond, second battle of Deep Bottom, battle of Chaffin's Farm, battle of Fair Oaks and Darbytown Road, battle of Fort Pillow, battle of Plymouth, battle of Cold Harbor, battle of Appomattox Court House, battle of the Crater, battle of Globe Tavern, battle of Peeble's Farm, battle of Boydton Plank Road, first battle of Fort Fisher, second battle of Fort Fisher, and Carolina's Campaign were the majority of the campaigns that the grandchildren of Harry and Kate Freeman fought in. Their contribution and the contribution of over two hundred thousand members of the United States Color Troops showed the country their commitment to the country despite how the country was treating them.

US Color Troops had paroled over thirty thousand confederate soldiers at Appomattox. Paroling soldiers was the process of them swearing allegiance to the United States and never taking up arms against it again. They were also part of the army that brought the Civil War to an end with the surrender of General Joe Johnston in North Carolina.

William Freeman had taken his leave from his position with Secretary of State Seward and fought with the 39th Regiment United States Color Troops. He was wounded at the Second Battle of Fort Fischer, sent to City Point, Virginia, then to the Washington, DC, area for medical attention. Given that the war was close to a favorable conclusion and the severity of his wounds, William was permitted to return to service for the Secretary of State William Seward.

It was a great homecoming celebration in Auburn and Washington for William Freeman's return to a normal life. William treated his return as if he had been away on an adventure and was now back home to carry on his business for the Freemans and Sewards. William enjoyed his responsibilities with Secretary of State William Seward. As the secretary's coachman, he was continuously being exposed to an assortment of interesting individuals.

William carried himself with great deportment, and no matter how interesting, controversial or contentious conversations were around him, he never allowed his body language or facial expressions to give any indication of interest or disinterest. While professional decorum was always maintained, if queried by Secretary Seward, William was always prepared to provide intuitive insights to the secretary. Secretary of State Seward and the Civil War veteran William Freeman developed a fond professional relationship and personal relationship. The war was coming to an end, and Seward was redirecting his attention to issues that could have major impact on the soon to be unified United States of America.

Seward was keeping a close eye on the Maximilian I's situation in Mexico. At the beginning of the Civil War European powers had taken advantage of our civil turmoil and seized the opportunity to violate the Monroe Doctrine which was the United States' way of keeping foreign interference out of North America.

With the advent of the Civil War in the United States, Napoleon III seized upon the opportunity to set up a pro-French monarchy in Mexico. He did this in collaboration with Austria, England, Spain. In the latter part of 1861 France, along with England and Spain, invaded Mexico and placed the younger brother of the Austrian Empire's, Emperor Franz Joseph, on the throne of the second Mexican Empire as Maximilian the First.

Mexican President Benito Juarez had maintained the fight against this armed take over. The United States' government was unable to assist President Juarez and the Mexican people during the conflict between the states. Now that the Civil War was in its final days, Secretary of State Seward had ramped up the government's assistance to Juarez.

Secretary Seward had been meeting with a delegation from the Juarez administration in exile and with the Secretary traveling to these meetings was his steward and coachman William Freeman. Mexico was on the verge of a total end all conflict with the people of Mexico on one side and on the other side French Empire, Maximillian's Mexican Empire, Austria, Belgium, Confederate exiles, Egypt, Polish exiles, Spain, and the United Kingdom.

Also, William Freeman was finding himself spending more time in the presence of Russians. It was clear that Secretary Seward was developing something of major concern. That item of major concern was the negotiation of land north of Canada called Alaska. Alaska was a wilderness that wasn't very relevant at that time, but President Lincoln and Secretary Seward wanted to secure the most northern entry into North America from intrusion by foreign powers.

Richmond, the capital of the Confederacy, had fallen, and to the chagrin of the secretary of state, President Lincoln was on his way to Richmond. Seward was concerned about Lincoln's personal safety. With the Confederacy having no possibility of victory, radical elements could believe that assassination was the only acceptable mode of revenge. In one of their quiet moments, Secretary Seward had expressed his concern about the president's safety to William.

William told the secretary, "Three things I learned by being in the war was you turn your safety over to the Lord, or it would be impossible to move forward, and that Mr. Lincoln was just as much a soldier as I was. He lived in the telegraph office, living every moment of the war, but his mission was different than mine. While my mission was to take that confederate position, his mission was to unify the nation and bring peace. His concern for his personal safety was secondary to his mission of unifying and bringing peace to our country."

Washington was bustling with cannon fire and fireworks of delight at the news of Richmond falling. Secretary Seward was making plans for a trip to Richmond, and William Freeman was looking forward to the trip because several of his relatives were part of the occupying forces, including his cousin Lewis, Uncle Luke's son, whom he hadn't seen since Uncle Luke's funeral.

Before leaving for Richmond it was time for the secretary's frequent coach ride with his children. As they were traveling, William noticed the carriage door was not closed properly. Before William could return to his seat, the horses bolted. William was thrown out of his seat still holding the reins. Secretary Seward and his son Fred jumped out of the carriage to stop the runaway horses. While jumping out the carriage, Seward stumbled and crashed to the pavement. A soldier helped William stop the frightened horse and helped Freeman carry the unconscious Secretary Seward back to his house.

Seward had been hurt badly. He had broken his jaw and his shoulder and didn't look like himself because of the severe bruising and discoloration of his face. Mr. Seward stayed unconscious for a long while sending fear through his family that he might not survive. William Freeman had sustained some cuts and bruises and a sprained knee in the carriage melee but refused any medical attention saying, "Compared to some of the injuries I encountered working with my father, this is no worse than getting a splinter."

While William Seward was recuperating, William Freeman returned to Auburn to take care of family business. With all the men having been away fighting in the Civil War, the Freeman businesses and New Guinea proper were in disarray. The family was in debt, and it looked like they would have to sell large tracts of New Guinea to cover their debts. The debts included the possibility of forfeiting their land because of increased taxes and conniving schemes from the white business element in Auburn.

The war was over, and thousands of people of color, women and men who had sacrificed and died for this Union called the United States of America, did so without still being given their rights as human beings and as citizens of these United States. Black Americans, Native Americans, Hispanic Americans, Asian Americans, and Pacific Islanders had proved their allegiance, bravery, and commitment to the ideals presented in the constitution.

No leaders of the government could deny these facts. The exclusion of what should have never been permitted, slavery, would not be enough. These people of color wanted the rights enjoyed by the white population. Though the struggle for those rights would continue, these brave man and women of valor kindled a fire that still burns bright.

PROOF ENOUGH!
Lift ev'ry voice and sing
Till earth and heaven ring.
Ring with the harmonies of Liberty.
Let our rejoicing rise,
High as the list'ning skies,
Let it resound loud as the rolling sea.
Sing a song full of the faith that the dark past has taught us,

Sing a song full of the hope that the present has brought us;
Facing the rising sun of our new day begun,
Let us march on till victory is won.

Stony the road we trod,
Bitter the chast'ning rod,
Felt in the days when hope unborn had died;
Yet with a steady beat,

Have not our weary feet,
Come to the place for which our fathers sighed?

We have come over a way that with tears has been watered,
We have come, treading our path through the blood of the slaughtered,
Out of the gloomy past,
Till now we stand at last Where the white gleam of our bright star is cast.

God of our weary years,
God of our silent tears,
Thou who has brought us thus far on the way;
Thou who has by Thy might,
Led us into the light,
Keep us forever in the path, we pray.
Lest our feet stray from the places, our God, where we met Thee,
Lest our hearts, drunk with the wine of the world, we

forget Thee,
Shadowed beneath thy hand,
May we forever stand,
True to our God,
True to our native land.
(James Weldon Johnson, 1919)

17

GONE ON THE WINDS

The world of New Guinea was changing rapidly as William witnessed on his return home after Secretary Seward's carriage accident. The unifying glue that kept all the inhabitants of New Guinea was their opposition to the evils that permeated from the issue of slavery. The 13th Amendment had outlawed slavery and was now only in need of ratification by the states which now, in April 1865, would be a done deal. The Underground Railroad Movement had completed its mission; the abolishment of slavery and the hope on the winds was that racism had been abated and that all Americans could be respected and treated the same. The "Winds of Hope" were the harbingers of a new United States that could finally reflect our written edicts of belief.

William was going to have to help his parents with the changing directions of the Freed Slavery Colony known as New Guinea. No longer needed as a safe terminal on the Underground Railroad, its popularity for newly emancipated slaves waned. During the Civil War many residents of New Guinea gained the independence they had desired and moved freely to expanding locations without fear of retribution from either slave catchers or slave owners.

Even the sense of family unity was dissipating as Freeman family members left New Guinea to explore personal concepts of venture, freedom, and growth. The old ways were gone, and in order to go forward, Platt and Mary would have to sell some of the Freemans' property. The hopes of African Americans were sailing on the gentle winds that had been generated by President of the United States Abraham Lincoln's equal treatment, equal rights, and equal opportunities for all citizens.

Nine days after Secretary Seward's carriage accident those gentle breezes of hope turned into a typhoon producing a hailstorm of hate and vengeance. A vicious storm that would blow positive hopes out to sea, continue a civil divide, and be responsible for the deaths of many more Americans. It would prolong the belief that the color of your skin gives you the right to supersede the mandates of God.

John Wilkes Booth shot and killed the president of the United States of America, Abraham Lincoln. The assassination of President Lincoln was part of a conspiracy to murder Lincoln, Vice President Johnson, and Secretary of State Seward. Booth succeeded in his attempt, and the assassin assigned to Johnson decided not to proceed with his attempt, but Lewis Powell came to the door seeking entrance as a delivery man of medicine from the doctor. On being denied admittance to the house by the servant at the door, Powell pushed past him and proceeded upstairs where Seward was still in bed recuperating from the carriage accident nine days earlier.

Fred Seward, the secretary's son, met Powell at the top of the stairs and was severally injured in his fight with the intruder. Powell injured Seward's son Augustus and the soldier assigned to protect Seward while trying to deliver death blows with his knife to Seward's neck area. One thrust had completely ripped Seward's cheek, and subsequent blows would have killed him if it wasn't for the metal neck brace he was wearing to help with his injuries from the carriage accident. When Augustus went to retrieve a pistol, Lewis Powell escaped the house.

Secretary Seward was bloody and disfigured by the attack, but the real concern was for his son Frederick. Fred's skull had been severely damaged by a blow to his head and whether he would survive or not was an extended question. Upon hearing of the attack on Seward and the assassination of the president, William Freeman immediately returned to Washington. The concerns of

New Guinea and the Freeman family would have to wait until this crisis subsided.

When William returned to the Seward home in Washington, his heart was torn given the sight and condition of the secretary and Frederick. On closer observation of the Seward family, Mrs. Seward appeared to be the one in greatest peril. Frances Seward had been in fragile health over the last few years. With the onset of the carriage accident, which caused her to hastily travel from Auburn to Washington, and now the bodily injury done to her husband and sons and the guard her resolve was strong in the presence of others, but her countenance was growing weaker in her private moments. Frances would say, "If I had two hearts, one would be beating for William and one would be beating for Frederick." Her faith in God to pull her family through this crisis gave her tired persona the strength to preserve the entire family, though her physical strength was ebbing. Frances succumbed to the stress and anguish, and she passed two months after the attack on William and Frederick in Washington.

It was a long train ride for the Sewards, bringing their matriarch's remains back to Auburn for burial. Adding to the pain was the absence of Frederick. He was still too ill to be exposed to such a venture. William Seward, still recuperating from the carriage accident and the assassination attempt, kept the family grounded in their loss by constantly reminding them of God's gifting to them of Frances Miller Seward and what her spirituality, love, concern for all people, and adherence to God's Way of Life has molded them to be who they are today.

William Freeman was William Seward's steward and coachman. They had been together a long time, except for Freeman's involvement in the Civil War. Because of the meaningful time they shared, pertinent conversation between them had blossomed into a way of life, particularly after Frances's death.

This would become extremely important as they returned to Washington and watched the gentle breezes of hope that the Lincoln administration had for the country get blown away by blizzard winds of greed and hate. There was nothing left for them to do but grind out the turmoil in the Andrew Johnson administration and then leave Washington forever.

18

END OF A SEASON

Before they had left Washington, Secretary of State Seward suffered another major blow. His only beloved daughter Fanny had passed from tuberculosis. Seward's anguish was great, but being the strong man of faith that he had exhibited time and time again, he was able to find peace in the Lord's decision to bring his baby girl home. While being at peace with God's decision to bring Frances and Fanny home, it was quite evident that there was a big hole in his heart with their deaths. He became more resolved to solitude and introspective flashes of reliving happier moments with William Freeman as it related to his departed love ones. Freeman made sure his library of remembrances was filled so not to have to repeat the same experience over and over. Seward truly appreciated Freeman's efforts in helping him maintain a presence of Frances and Fanny.

Upon returning to Auburn, William Freeman discovered the Free Slave Colony of New Guinea was no more.

The Underground Railroad Movement had concluded its function with the passage of the 13th, 14th and 15th Amendments to the constitution. The ready-made supply of runaway slaves ready to work had ended, and many of those residents of New Guinea were moving on to new ventures. His relatives were now more inclined to maintain their own private properties away from the New Guinea homestead, and many had decided to move away from Auburn.

The season had truly come to an end for the way the Freeman family lived in Auburn. Too many family members were too busy feasting off the storehouses of over seventy years of family building and growth without contributing anything back for the general wellbeing of the family. They felt entitled. They believed that they had the right to consume all the golden eggs and the golden goose for their own self-aggrandizement.

William Freeman seeing this change in his ancestral home among his own family in Auburn and remembering that our country had just ended a season which it was born with, slavery, it was clear the new season for the Freemans and the United States of America was yet to be defined.

William knew that these new definitions were in God's Hands and only his faith and willingness to walk in the path that God had set before him would make it possible for him to make it through what was going to be troubling times and accept God's timing. He remembered what his father told him and what his grandfather would tell him, "Boy, you've got to learn to be patient. God don't set his clock by your pocket watch."

What William did know was that those stumps behind the old praise house was the place where troubled Freemans gained clarity from the Lord on how to go forward in this mean old-world God's Way.

The praise house was in need of serious repair. Having brought an AME Zion Church to Auburn, the little praise house's purpose had been fulfilled, and now it was being left for the ages, but the allure of the stumps behind it still remained. The call directing William to those old shiny stumps was that of his forefathers and mothers that needed to find "true north" on their "compasses of life" in order to trod the right path of life in service to God and their family.

William took a seat on his favorite stump, the one where he would sit with his siblings for many hours listening to his father Platt telling them about Harry and Kate's history in Africa, in captivity, in freedom in England and the colonies. Platt would remind them never to forget their history because it would be their history if they failed to keep God first in everything that you do. Platt told his children, "At their individually lowest points in captivity, your grandparents promised God that if He freed them from this hellacious bondage that they and their children and their children's children and all the future children sprouted from our seed by us would serve you our God. My children, you have been dedicated to God. If you want the blessings in Deuteronomy, the 28th chapter, accept the fact that you have been dedicated to God, then you will receive the blessings of God. If you chose to refuse to accept your dedication of service to God, then you will be exposed to the curses of Deuteronomy, the 28th chapter, as God deems fit to place on you."

This dedication of his life to God in service to God kept William from straying too far from the path he knew God had laid out for him, but stray he did. Now it was time for him to get in alignment with God.

"Father, I'm lost. We have struggled with slavery and the hateful disease of racism. Now, when slavery has been defeated and it looks like racism has no place to take root, men are in the midst of creating new systems to maintain their earthly benefits derived from the bondage of others. They are planting new fields of racism and divisive fears that are wrong, yet they call themselves followers of You! Their actions belie any truth or commitment to your tenets. Their meanness and hatred are turning my heart away from You. I'm in a quandary, help me Lord!" William cried unto God.

"My son, I have already given you the answer to these concerns of yours. The problem is you need to refer to the answers I have established instead of trying to define a new solution to ages-old human concern. I've already taught you how to address that problem of dealing with people who have not submitted to my will for their lives yet, 'Let both grow together until the harvest. Then I will tell the harvesters to sort out the weeds, tie them into bundles, and burn them, and to put the wheat in the barn,'" (Matt. 13-30, NLT) responded the Lord.

"But, Lord, these people stand for everything you are against. Why must I be subject to their abuse?" William screamed.

"'Always be humble and gentle. Be patient with each other, making allowance for each other's faults because of your love. Make every effort to keep yourself united in the Spirit, binding yourselves together with peace.' (Ephesians 4:2&3, NLT) Remember that they're my children, too, and I'm still working on them," offered the Lord.

"Lord, what principle, what way, could I possibly be united with these mean and hateful people that go against everything you want? People who degrade and kill? People who literally worship money and the earthly power it gives them? People who have a thousand lambs and connive and cheat to take the one from a poor man?

People who say you are sovereign on Sunday and spend the rest of the week working for the devil? People who hate me or feel I'm inferior because of the color of my skin? What am I supposed to unite with these people about?" William asked.

"THAT I AM THE GREAT I AM, and I am God all by myself. There is the origin of change I need you to unite with others on. I'll take it from there," instructed the Lord.

"Enough said, Lord. Thy Will be Done!" exclaimed William in total submission.

"Therefore, since we are surrounded by such a huge crowd of witnesses to the life of faith, let us strip off every weight that slows us down, especially the sin that so easily trips us up. And let us run with endurance the race God has set before us. We do this by keeping our eyes on Jesus, the champion who initiates and perfects our faith. Because of the joy awaiting him, he endured the cross disregarding its shame. Now he is seated in the place of honor beside God's throne. Think of all the

hostility he endured from sinful people, then you won't become weary and give up. After all, you have not yet given your lives in your struggle against sin."

(Hebrew 12: 1-4, NLT)

19

SEWARD'S and FREEMAN'S GOBAL TOUR

William Freeman was preparing for an adventure that would rival Grandpa Harry's adventures with John Hardenbergh. William and the secretary were about to engage in a trip around the world. A trip that would keep them away from Auburn for well over a year. The task was enormous. Since the secretary was a man of habit, it would be William's responsibility to assure that those things of necessity were included in the travel baggage plus his own needs.

There would be no running back to Auburn from Calcutta to get anything. They had gotten their feet wet with the transcontinental trip they took last year with Seward's children, his deceased daughter's best friend Olive Risley, her father Hanson Risley, and Olive's sister Harriet Risley. The secretary had become very close to Olive since the death of his daughter Fanny. Now it was time to take this world tour. Hanson Risley would not be participating in this excursion, but his two daughters would be accompanying them, along with Seward's nephew George and his wife; they would be with them until China. George Seward was appointed the new ambassador to China. Olive will be chronicling the global tour, and her sister was going to help with the illustration. Another couple would be making the journey also.

William, along with his personal duties for the secretary, was also the unofficial tour coordinator. Everyone that knew the secretary knew that the closest human being to him outside of his children was William Freeman. Seward trusted Freeman to assure that everything would be in the right place at the right time at every location. They were friends, and they worked well together.

William had prepared everything that was important for him and the secretary to be gone from home for the duration of this tour but knew he wanted to spend some time with his family and closest friends.

William had a great time with family and friends, but his greatest enjoyment came sitting at the feet of those friends of the family that he called his aunts and uncles. They were people who valued what his family was trying to accomplish and had committed themselves to more than their personal wellbeing. These included men he called uncle like Daniel Hughes, Frederick Douglas,

Martin Delaney, and William Still and women of great fortitude that he called aunt like Sojourner Truth, Frances Seward, Frances Harper, Amelia Bloomer, Pricilla Baltimore, and Harriet Tubman.

Aunt Harriet was "God's soldier on earth." She had one mission and one mission only, and that was to serve God. She would tell Catherine Freeman and Mary Freeman, "You know that general in Joshua 5:13? The one Joshua asked, 'Are you friend or foe?' and he told Joshua, 'Neither, I am the General of God's Army'? Well, I'm his colonel."

Aunt Harriet took a liking to Mary and Platt's son William as a small boy when she was conducting her business for the Underground Railroad Movement, even before she settled in Auburn. She saw something in that young William Freeman and thought she might be able to nurture it a little. Harriet Tubman had a smile that came from her soul and could light up a dim room that was only reserved for family and select moments. William and Aunt Harriet spent a great deal of time on those stumps behind the praise house worshipping the Lord.

Auntie would tell William, "Son, people spend more time praising God than they do worshiping God. How are you going to listen to what you are supposed to do while you're running your mouth?" Young William would just nod in agreement with his Auntie Harriet.

"I ain't got no time for these games people want to play," Harriet would tell young William. "They want me to smile more. Smile about what? Most of them have mixed their own wants and desires in with the mission God has given them. I'll work with them, but I don't trust them. William, how you going to trust somebody that think they know better than God?"

"I don't know, Auntie. I guess you stay on guard around them, then ask the Lord what you should do," William responded.

"That's right, boy!" Harriet declared with a big smile of approval. "They want me to be more cordial, attend important gatherings, change my attire, and look more delicate. They are out of their minds. What little I do do, I do it to bring support and money to our cause."

Harriet stood up and gazed over the bank of the Owasco Outlet, watching its waters breaking over the rocks below, and turned slightly towards William while chewing on a stalk of wild grass and told young Freeman, "They think I do something special. They think that getting hit in the head has somehow made me some kind of different human being that has a special hearing ability of God's directives. Shoot, all I did was get sick and tired of human responses to my concerns and desires and surrender my will to do God's Will."

She walked back to the stump alongside of William and put her arms around him and said, "All these people think that I'm this mean, bad, pistol-toting wild woman when all I really wanted was my family and peace and not to be judged by the color of my skin. All I wanted to do was to serve my God. All those trips I took to bring freedom and peace to others I have never had to shoot anybody. Don't get me wrong, there were several times I felt that a person deserved death, but it wasn't what God wanted. William, my boy, there was nothing special about your Auntie. I ain't no explorer like Lewis and Clark, and I'm not a warrior like Winfield Scott. I just turn left when the Lord says turn left and turn right when the Lord says turn right and cross here when the Lord says cross here and stop when the Lord says stop and go when the Lord says go. It's as simple as that. Obedience to the Will of God for my life was the key to my life. William, my boy, it will be the key to your life if you let it."

As William sat there behind the old, dilapidated praise house reminiscing about all his Auntie had taught him and shared with him, he found himself embraced from behind with a strong hug of strength by one of the smallest human beings he knew, his Aunt Harriet. She had sent word for William to meet her there in order to catch up on what was happening to him and to hear about his adventures with Secretary Seward.

William shared the integral details of his personal life with his Auntie and informed her of his and the secretary's pending global tour. Harriet was happy that things were going so well in William's life; she was happy about her family, and she was happy about her church work, but the one thing that was troubling her was that the army was denying her pension from the Civil War. She had no income. She had a few benefactors that helped, but she had plans for taking care of those who couldn't take care of themselves. Her only source of income was walking through Auburn with a basket on her arm selling the produce from her land. William promised to see what he could do or inspire concerning about her pension.

William and Harriet sang to the Lord, prayed to the Lord, meditated on the Lord, and thanked the Lord. When they had finished their time with the Lord, they embraced, with Harriet praying a prayer of protection over William. William Freeman left his encounter with Harriet Tubman ready to take on the major task before him. He kissed Harriet bye and promised to return for a visit when he got back home.

His task was the preparation of Secretary Seward's world junket. Seward was bringing six other individuals along for this journey. They included his adopted daughter Olive Risley Seward, her sister Harriet Risley, Hanson Risley, Olive and Harriet's father who would only be traveling to San Francisco, his nephew George Seward who had been appointed ambassador to China and his wife, and Alexander Randall and his wife, a couple of Seward's acquaintances. Even though George and his wife would be departing the entourage in China, William would still be responsible for their baggage and their gathering of souvenirs and trinkets until then and Mr. Risley's property too. This was going to be a major undertaking that could turn into a logistical nightmare. William would have only two trusted staff members with him on this expedition, Jenny Corell and Arthur Price. Their coordination of services was going to become extremely important, especially when modes of transportation became more primitive and roads and hilly terrain became obstacles. In addition, they would be engaging with individuals who spoke little or no English.

What was going to make William's job less complicated and easier to administrate was the declaration that the secretary had made according to Mr. Freeman's authority, "Everyone must listen to and follow the directions of Mr. Freeman." This was a novel notion in the United States of America that white Americans had to officially follow the edicts of a black American.

William was constantly addressing the issue of him and his people having to be slaves in the colonies and the United States proper. His father, Platt Freeman, had told him how his Grandfather Harry and Grandmother Kate would play the "slave game" with John Hardenbergh in order to achieve their goals without ignorant impediments. William appreciated what they had done in order to give him the opportunities he had been afforded, but his pride was offended to accept their opinion that his family accomplishments could not have been achieved without being happy slaves that needed a handout from a good white master until God spoke to him behind the praise house.

"Your forefather and foremother cried out to me when they were captive slaves in Africa. They made an oath to me that if I would end this misery of slavery in their lives that they and all future generations of their children would also serve me. I sent a great wind to free them in the middle of my great sea. They were never to be slaves on any land as long as they served me, the Great I Am that I Am. My son, your pride wants to shout 'I'm free,' but freedom only comes from submission to my Will for your life. There is nothing worse than a Free-Man or Free-Woman who is enslaved spiritually."

This intervention by the Lord brought William the clarity he needed and the ability to follow (Eph 4:2); basically, love them anyway, but it still amazed him the absurdities that the devil could conjure up in those not working on improving their relationship with God.

William found it amazing that many individuals believed that black Americans had become whole individuals with the passing of the 15th Amendment. That they were no longer two-thirds of a human being and now could learn how to have a family and be responsible members of their American society. They gave no consideration to how difficult it was for African Americans to maintain a family and to be included in what they had contributed to make the United States of America. Now it became a common novelty to quiz any African American whose deportment resembled that of a white American on how he or she was able to obtain such values and skills in such a short time given the passage of the 15th Amendment.

This was like fingernails screeching across a blackboard to William Freeman. Societal beliefs that the amendments established to rectify the wrongs promulgated by our culture have created this "Modern Prometheus," or as Mary Shelly termed it, Frankenstein. It was as if feeling, loving, caring, producing, commitment, devotion, and spirituality had just been incorporated into these black Americans, whether free or slave, with their incorporation.

It appeared not to be a literal interpretation. Now that they are no longer two-thirds of a person but a whole person, as according to the Dred Scott Decision, and have the right to vote, they can be contributors to every aspect of American Society at last. No, too many people had a figurative interpretation, that African Americans were totally without family, perspectives, understanding of the world around them, and until the 15th Amendment, Blacks only had only two-thirds of insight, understanding, ability, and political awareness and expected these newly made complete Americans to not have interest or understanding of the world around them.

This was truly a major problem for William Freeman and a matter of dislike for William Seward. Secretary Seward, at the first appearance of this backward thinking, would invite the victim into a game of understanding that would impact their lives forever. Mr. Seward would summon Mr. Freeman and would ask the individual where they thought Mr. Freeman was from with his European-style clothing and his impeccable deportment. After attempting to guess their way to a solution Mr. Freeman would begin to recant and share the story of his family coming to the colonies and living and helping to build the United States of America. By this time Mr. Seward had walked off and left those unaware individuals captivated by this erudite Black American named William Freeman.

Secretary Seward's willingness to correct the misgivings of others towards African Americans helped reduce the ignorance of other people from a problem to an annoyance. This would be extremely important on this journey as Seward and Freeman traveled to places where African Americans, whether freed or enslaved, had only been read about.

It was a warm August day when the Seward entourage began its voyage extraordinaire. William's concern was the next days out because there would be intermediate stops requiring certain pieces of baggage to be available more readily. This required William to get his staff to share the itinerary with Mr. Seward's guests and find out their specific needs for the week. Instead of taking a route through the United States to Detroit, going through Canada provided the most direct route because of the lack of population.

William was looking forward to the stop in Chatham, Canada; his cousin Harriet Dubois lived there. Chatham, Canada, was a major terminal on the Underground Railroad; many of their residents had come through New Guinea while William was growing up. As they crossed the new bridge at Niagara Falls moving into Canada, they were greeted by Mr. Clifton from the United States' Consulate Office. There was a very warm reception for Mr. Seward and his entourage that consisted mostly of former slaves that had migrated to Canada. When William stepped off the train, he was mobbed by a group of well-wishers that wanted the latest news about his family and Auburn. After several minutes of exchanging information with the general crowd William noticed a small group of men standing off to the side. There was something familiar about those men, but it wasn't till they started to sing an old familiar song that he realized they were childhood friends whose parents had settled first in New Guinea for several years. Their reunion was bright and filled with great frivolity. It was difficult for William to board the train and depart.

They reentered the United States in Detroit and proceeded toward the Missouri River. It was necessary to cross the Missouri River by ferry. During that portion of their trip a group of travelers where engaged in an intense conversation about world affairs and thought it would be interesting to get the opinion of an African American who had just achieved his citizenship through the 15th Amendment. William immediately provided them details and insights they had never considered. They were totally amazed at the depth of his knowledge, balanced judgement on matters and insight into matters that were still mysteries to them. They were totally amazed that William Freeman, a newly certified citizen of the United States, apparently was already as qualified to talk about matters as any white person. William was glad that the Lord and him had those conversations behind the praise house. They truly prepared him for these situations.

The excursion continued across the country, occasionally placing great demand on Freeman and his staff, but they were able to meet every challenge presented. When they got to Utah, Brigham Young provided Mr. Seward and his entourage an overview of what the Church of Latter Days Saints had accomplished in Utah.

Brigham was an old acquaintance of Seward and the Freeman Family. Brigham was from the Port Byron area and had painted the Seward mansion as an apprentice to Mr. Jeffries while Judge Miller was still alive. He also had learned to love those lunches William's grandmother use to make and her rhubarb pie. Brigham also had a working relationship with William's dad Platt when he was working at the bucket company in Port Byron. Brigham Young provided them a warm welcome, but it was time to move on.

They continued across the Pacific Ocean to Japan where Mr. Seward and Mr. Freeman had a major laugh recounting the story told to them by a Japanese official about a tycoon who had recently usurped power in Japan. Mr. Seward was startled by such news and quizzed the official about how recent this event had taken place. The official said, "Six hundred years ago." Mr. Seward struggled to maintain a straight face, and Mr. Freeman turned to the side so he wouldn't betray the moment. When they were alone Mr. Seward said, "Mr. Freeman, with our country not even one hundred years old, it is sometimes hard to measure time in these ancient societies."

Japan was the first port of call for this Seward's Global Adventure. Yokohama, Kanagawa, Yeddo, Osaka, and Nagasaki were some of the places Seward's entourage visited. While in Japan, the Tenno, the Heavenly Emperor, was going to receive Mr. Seward at his summer house in the Great Castle. Mr. Walsh from the United States Consulate Office in Japan and Mr. Freeman accompanied Mr. Seward. As they passed through the third inner wall of the Great Castle, Mr. Walsh and Mr. Freeman were informed that they could proceed no further because they were "unofficial gentlemen.". The stern appearance of the guards made it clear that this was not a debatable issue. So, Mr. Freeman and Mr. Walsh remained "unofficial gentlemen" the rest of that day.

The Seward party was on the steamship *Shan Tung* in route to China. While in travel, a young marine approached Mr. Freeman's office and related an intriguing story to him. This young marine had been assigned to protect Seward's home the night of the assassination attempt on his life, the same night President Lincoln was killed. He also was part of the detachment that accompanied Mr. Seward and Mr. Freeman to Alaska last year.

He had approached Mr. Freeman in the hopes of finally gaining an opportunity to meet Mr. Seward. Mr. Freeman went to Admiral John Rodgers and informed him of his marine's intent. The admiral concurred with Mr. Freeman, and a meeting was arranged. The young marine, Mr. Seward, and Mr. Freeman spent a delightful hour together.

China was the next stop: Hong Kong, Canton, Tien-Tsin, Peking, Shanghai, Woosung, Chee Foo, the Great Wall, and more. Mr. Seward and Mr. Freeman were looking forward to this segment of the trip. They were going to be reunited with two old friends, Chi-Tajen and Sun-Tajen. Chi-Tajen and Sun-Tajen were Chinese performers who had conducted performances in Auburn, New York, at Seward's bequest. That would surely be a delightful gathering for both Seward and Freeman.

In Shanghai, Mr. Seward and Mr. Freeman met a very interesting, humble, and delightful Black man named Mr. Butler. Mr. Butler was from Washington, DC, where he had been born a slave to Commodore Rodgers, the father of Admiral John Rodgers. Mr. Butler was in charge of the entire freighting business of the Shanghai Steam Navigation Company. Mr. Butler had been accepted for his giftings and not rejected because of the complexion of his skin. It was learned that Mr. Butler had an annual salary of four thousand dollars a year.

Shanghai also alerted Mr. Seward to a situation that just a few months earlier would have required his full attention as secretary of state for the United States of America. The second Empire of France had been overthrown. Mr. Seward was bombarded by questions about whether the Orleans Dynasty or the elder branch of the Bourbons would secure power. Mr. Seward responded, "I believe henceforth that France will be a republic. They have experimented with a monarchy and a dictatorship and found that neither worked for them." On and on they went in China, navigating on the Pei-ho River in a flotilla of flat-bottom boats and taking in five thousand years of history.

Organization and logistics of the entourage's baggage and numerous giftings from dignitaries and the common people was a nightmare. The man up for the task was Mr. Freeman. When it was time to get stern, he was stern. He wasn't afraid to pitch in and show how it was done correctly. No matter what the situation or the difficulty, Mr. Freeman would devise a solution. This led people in the entourage to refer to him as "Faithful Mr. Freeman."

Saigon, Singapore, Java, Ceylon, Pondicherry, Madras, Calcutta, Benares, Sarnath, Bombay, Delhi, Umballa, Himalayas, Goa, Hindosian, Arcot, on and on they went. In Java, Mr. Seward and Mr. Freeman were confronted with the questions around the 15th amendment. Mr. Seward invited them to quiz Mr. Freeman, and when

Mr. Freeman had finished, they were amazed and dumb-founded by the eloquent substance that Mr. Freeman had imparted to their knowledge base. In India, discussion around the 15th Amendment would again surface, this time being recorded in international newspapers.

The Maharajah of Putteeala had arranged for a sixty-elephant excursion for the Seward entourage. Mr. Freeman, who was mounted on the last elephant, received no assistance in dismounting the elephant. He was left on top of the elephant while the banquet was going on. Mr. Seward eventually noticed Mr. Freeman's absence and inquired about his whereabouts. Mr. Freeman was found still perched on his elephant. Well, the media immediately queried Mr. Seward about how Mr. Freeman was treated as he was a new citizen of the United States and Mr. Freeman interceded with the Maharajah to keep the attendant from receiving severe punishment for his dereliction of duty. It appears that the attendant seeing Mr. Freeman as a man of color like him assumed that Mr. Freeman knew how to dismount the animal and was just taking his time to do it.

Arabia, Aden, Egypt, Palestine, Cairo, Thebes, Assouan, Assiout, Philae, Jerusalem, Jaffa-Ramleh, Lydda, Athens, Constantinople, Hungary, Austria, Italy, Florence, Rome, the Vatican, Naples, Switzerland, France,

Paris, Versailles, Hamburg, London, Montrose on the Hudson, and so many more stops; Seward's Global Adventure was truly one to rival time and immemorial.

Mr. Freeman's major keepsakes from this adventure were two major events. He had always wanted to see the treasures of East Africa. William thought exploring the pyramids, sphinxes, and obelisks of Egypt, the Sudan, and Ethiopia would be extremely rewarding. Unfortunately, Ethiopia would not be on their itinerary. Such places, like the Lalibela Church Complex in Ethiopia, would have to remain just a mental image from books and pictures.

The first event was in Assiout while they were exploring a pyramid. All the mental visions of a mysterious place of intrigue and wonder soon vanished in the reality of a dark, dank hole with fetid air filled with darting bats and hooting owls eager to startle you at every turn. During the exploration of the pyramid at Assiout, Mr. Freeman's foot slipped, and he fell five feet to another level in the dark. Mr. Freeman wasn't hurt, but it provided the group a suitable rationale to end the tour of the pyramid without offending their host. Everyone left with a common belief that pyramids are best viewed from the outside.

The second event was at Philae where they concluded their voyage up the Nile River. It was customary to carve an inscription into the granite rock. Mr. Freeman carved his name into that rock with the hope that one day a future child might discover his name and add their name. It would be a historical perspective that would last forever. Little did William realize that his actions when he returned home would cause people to recite his name in response to "Service to Others" for generations to come.

20

THE CLARITY OF TIME

The whirlwind trip was over. Mr. Freeman was amazed at how well Mr. Seward's stamina had not betrayed him during their global adventure. Now the luster was beginning to dissipate from his persona. Mr. Seward was tired. A year after their return, he was working at his desk when he took ill and developed difficulties breathing. Mr. Seward was surrounded by his family and Mr. Freeman as he spoke his last words, "Love each other."

Time brings clarity that a person needs to go forward. You can't go forward while looking at what used to be. New Guinea was no more. It had been the vision of Harry and Kate that came to fruition, served its purpose, and now was just a memory. The Freed Slave Colony had admirably fulfilled its role as a station and terminal for the Underground Railroad without fanfare or notoriety. The Freemans had been "purpose driven." They cemented a way of life that made the family's future first.

Now the family was a disjointed band of individuals that had mostly developed an opinion of entitlement.

William's mother Mary and his youngest brother John had moved from New Guinea to Division St. shortly after Platt's death over a decade earlier. It was impossible to manage and maintain the New Guinea homestead from afar. This was particularly true for Mary Freeman, an aging and health challenged black women with no support neither from her children nor close family members. All of Platt and Mary's children and all of Luke and Catherine's children were attempting to live their own lives independent of a collective approach through family.

Mary would say, "These children act like 'free-fingers.' They see all the success the hands had accomplished working together with the fingers, and they think they can achieve it all by themselves! They figured they don't need the hands. Their hands, who are their elders and their history, only impede them from the greatness and freedom that has been created by the devil in their minds for them. They just long to be free from everything associated with the hand and be a 'free-finger.' 'The world is waiting for me to be a 'free-finger'! Until they become a 'free-finger,' then they learn how inadequate, vulnerable, and unproductive they really are by themselves. You can't be a 'free-finger' and unlock what God has for you and what the Great I AM wants you to do."

Yes, New Guinea was gone because of legitimate reasons and illegitimate reasons. A place that William felt deserved a prominent place of honor in the memory of the country, Auburn, and himself. There was no need to walk the land that brought him so much joy in his youth and wish things were different. It was time to end that chapter and get prepared to pen a new one. One whose direction could only be written clearly with the direction of God. William was going to have to work harder at getting out of God's Way for his life.

William found himself in his free time doing a great deal of traveling. On a trip visiting his cousin George Freeman in New Orleans he met a young lady named Laura Jones. Laura had been born during the Civil War in Jones County, Mississippi. She had been told that her parents had been a part of the Free State of Jones County, Mississippi, during the Civil War. They provided Newton Knight and his men supplies and information in the Piney Woods swamps. Her father had been lynched by the Ku Klux Klan for believing the 15th Amendment made him a complete citizen and gave him the right to vote.

William and Laura found each other very interesting. She enjoyed talking to a man that was insightful and knowledgeable. Laura and William took a liking to each other. Whatever rhyme or reason or official business would bring William to the deep South he always took it as an opportunity to communicate with Laura. Before too long, a full courtship had blossomed.

Returning home from his first encounter with Laura Jones he was very careful to maintain full secrecy around his family because he was thirty years old and had yet to start a family. He was tired of hearing about, "When are you going to settle down and start a family? You know, a man in a position like yours would be a great catch for some young lady." William had no attention of being a "great catch!" He had seen too many "great catches" turn into "great flops" in his family. He wanted love, and he knew God would guide that process. William only had one person he could confide in, his Auntie.

He always had been very careful in sharing his personal concerns and was tighter than a New England clam when it came to divulging any information professionally. Having been the steward and coachman to one of the most powerful men the United States, William H. Seward, and still in the employ of his family, people were always trying to get tidbits of information. Harriet Tubman was the only person he had confidence in to keep his concerns and thoughts private.

William decided to venture out to Harriet's property on South Street. It had been years since he had been out to her property. As he got closer, he was amazed at the army of children and people of all colors black, white, brown, red, and yellow milling about the yard. William smiled to himself and thought, Auntie is truly the Moses of her people.

The first person he greeted was Mama Rita, Harriet's mother, who was glad to see him and marveled over how he had grown into a fine young man. Mama Rita would get lost in the stories of the past and her friendship with the Freemans. If you had not learned how to escape during one of her "pregnant pauses," your entire day could be spent listening to the same stories she told during your last visit.

While he was sitting out front with Mama Rita, Nelson came out and gave him a great big bear hug. Nelson Davis was Harriet's husband. Nelson and William met after the war when Nelson first came to Auburn. William Freeman felt that Nelson Davis was a hero for what he and his fellow soldiers did at the Battle of Olustee in Florida.

The 54th USCT had gotten some attention due to Frederick's involvement. His own 39th USCT and a few others had received a little attention for their heroics around Petersburg, Richmond, and Appomattox, but the 8th, along with the 54th, took on a task that no other Union Regiment, White or Black, had to endure in the Civil War. The Battle of Olustee, or by the name most folks know it, the Battle of Ocean Pond, was fought in February 1864.

The Battle of Ocean Pond was fought in the Okefenokee Swamp in Baker County ten miles east of Lake City, Florida. The 8th USCT and the 54th USCT, 1st North Carolina Colored Volunteers (35th USCT after this battle), along with several other White regiments Hawley's Brigade, 7th Connecticut, 7th New Hampshire, 47th New York , 48th New York and 115th New York, and the 14th Massachusetts were sent to Jacksonville, Florida, to fortify the Union's position there under the command of General Truman Seymour. In skirmishes immediately outside of Jacksonville the Union troops encountered very light and disorganized resistance from area Confederate militias. This emboldened General Seymour to countermand his orders not to leave Jacksonville. He and 5,500 Union troops proceeded west with visions of disrupting the most important East-West railroad link in the Confederacy the Florida Atlantic and Gulf-Central Railroad and capturing Tallahassee the capitol of the state of Florida.

General Seymour was a very incompetent leader prone to not following orders and not seeking competent advice from his staff. General Seymour entered the fray in a piecemeal approach. He allowed two units to be completely inundated while having ten battle ready units sit and watch. His greatest incompetency was issuing wrong orders to the 7th New Hampshire which caused them to panic and flee the battlefield. This allowed the 8th USCT and the 1st North Carolina to be totally decimated by the confederate troops.

This was war, and these were occurrences that are associated with war, troops fleeing, flanks overrun, the "fog of war" occurs on battlefields. The real atrocities occurred after the Battle of Ocean Pond. Bands of confederate soldiers roamed the battlefield killing all wounded Black United States of America's soldiers and throwing their bodies into what is known as "Coonhead Swamp." It derived that derogatory name because the heads of the murdered unburied Black soldiers would bob up to the surface. To this very day, "Coonhead Swamp" is known to the Black residents of the Lake City, Florida, area. It is estimated that over five hundred United States Colored Troopers were murdered, and their corpses thrown into "Coonhead Swamp."

President Abraham Lincoln addressed how he felt about the contribution of these heroic Black soldiers on April 19, 1864: ***"There have been men who have proposed to me to return to slavery the black warriors of Port Hudson & Olustee to their masters to conciliate the South. I should be damned in time & eternity for doing so." (Abraham Lincoln, April 19, 1864)***

General Seymour was not to be denied his racial complicity in this entire Battle of Olustee aftermath.

Seymour had held the 54th USCT in reserve. They and the 1st North Carolina Colored Volunteers (35 USCT) where given the task of covering the retreat of the other Union regiments. In covering Seymour's withdrawal to Sanderson about three miles away with the 54th, the 1st lost nearly 240 men.

The train taking wounded Union soldiers from the battlefield back to Jacksonville, approximately fifty miles away, was completely segregated. Severity of wounds did not matter; the first train load of wounded was all white Union soldiers. Having achieved their primary function of covering the retreat, the 54th was informed that it would have to countermarch back to the battle area to pull the train which had broken down, back to Jacksonville over fifty miles away. The 54th and the 8th, who were protecting the train full of black Union soldiers, attached ropes to the locomotive and each car of the train and pulled the train east. When they reached the Union camp at Sanderson they were given horses to aid them.

The 54th and the 8th took several days to reach Jacksonville, but true to their commitment, they completed the task before them.

This was the type of man Nelson Davis was. He believed that if you watched his actions you would learn everything there is to know about Nelson Davis. Nelson had been a true godsend to Harriet's life and continued mission. The end of slavery did not end "The Moses of

Her People's" task. It just ended one phase and opened the door to start the next phase as given to her by God. This phase was going to require more than her fortitude and strength. Phase two required a bundle of earthly resources which she knew God would provide. God had given Harriet the only thing she ever wanted, that was to be loved. God sent Nelson Davis whose age difference with Harriet Tubman-Davis never diminished their love or affection for each other, and to complete their completeness, the Lord allowed them to adopt a little girl name Gert.

Harriet Tubman-Davis was personally grateful and satisfied with the love God sent her way. The fact that Harriet had started her new phase of work for the Lord was quite evident by the swarm of human beings either related to her, acquainted to her, or unknown to her congregating around her home.

William walked into the parlor and hollered, "Auntie!" Harriet's eyes gleamed with joy as she embraced William. They stayed locked in their embrace longer than most of the folks in the parlor expected. Those who had never met William before had an inquisitive look trying to figure out who this man was that could elicit such a greeting from Harriet.

Harriet and William took a walk outside on her property where there was an ancient tree and two chairs in its shade waiting for them. William asked Harriet what was going on with all the people at the house and on the property. Harriet assured him it was alright by sharing, "It's just some of my people in need."

She hadn't changed, and William knew she wasn't going to change as long as there was breath in her body. He had tried, along with the Sewards and a few of her most devoted patrons, to get Harriet to capitalize on her notoriety immediately after the Civil War, but she would have very little to do with that traveling and standing up in front of folks who don't want to hear what we got to do next for God. "All they want to hear is how wet and cold I was in those woods doing God's Work."

She could always get a big chuckle from William when she talked about what people wanted to hear instead of what they needed to hear. She would always start by looking around to make sure nobody else was listening, then lean into William and say, "Boy! Those people out there," waving her hand to her side and back. "Those people out there both white and black want to make my work for the Lord sound exciting. They what to know, 'What kind of pistols did I carry?' I tell them, 'Ones that shoot.' They don't want to hear about how cold that steel of that pistol can get and how many times I wanted to get rid of those heavy ice-cold pistols. They want me to sweeten everything up, so it excites their innards. They be wanting to know, 'Did you really threaten to shoot anyone that wanted to turn back?' 'Yep,' I tell them. I know my Bible."

She would pause there and look at William with a stern look she might have in the middle of the Wilderness and quizzed, "Boy, you know who Lot's wife is?" William would attempt to match her stern expression, but he had learned from years of trying that matching Harriet Tubman in stern looks was always a losing proposition. So, he would just respond, "Yes, Auntie I know who she is." Harriet would retort, "I've got enough sense to know that if God sends you on a mission and you turn away from that mission something bad is going to happen to you! All Lot's wife had to do was carry herself out of Sodom and Gomorrah and don't look back. Nah, she couldn't do that; she had to be disobedient. So, the Lord turned her into "a pillar of salt" just for looking back. Ain't no telling what God might have done to me for turning back or letting one of his people that He entrusted to me turn back. Son, what you think about that?"

"Auntie, I know you will never stray from the task that God gives you," her nephew retorted with complete devotion and belief.

Upon receiving the right response, she would lean back in her chair and resume, "People want to believe I was some real tough woman trying to be a man. People who want to hear about what I have to say have heard about Frances Harper and especially Aunt Polly Jackson. A powerful woman who fought off slave catchers with a butcher knife and boiling water and started a freed slave town in Ohio called Africa, Ohio. You know, boy, the AME Zion Church is always going to be our Spiritual Underground Railroad. It sure has given us strong women that have inspired me, like Mother Baltimore and Sojourner Truth, our friend. Then they look at pictures of me defiantly marching through swamps. They see pictures of me on wanted posters looking like one of those pirates on Captain Blackbeard's ship.

"Based on my so-called heroics and the embellishments placed on them over time, people expect to see a cross between Paul Bunyan, the lumberjack folklore, and John Henry, the steel-driven railroad folklore in a dress."

Harriet and William burst into earth-shaking laughter before Harriet continued, "Then I walk in no taller than Big Man Hughes' five-foot walking stick and no wider than a blade of grass. The first thing I see in their eyes is dejection because I don't meet their mind's expectations. Leave that traveling circus to Douglas, Harper, and Stills. I let Sarah Bradford do that book about me, but I haven't seen much income from it. All I know is that I've got to build a place for hurting people, and I know God will make a way."

William empathized with her, and then he attempted to convince her to get back on the speaking circuit. He explained to her how that would be the quickest way to increase the resources for her next commission project for the Lord. He told her, "You using what God had already placed in your hands is like Shamgar killing six hundred Philistines with an ox goad in the Bible."

Harriet nodded with a slight glimpse of approval and then asked how he was doing. William told her he was in love with a little southern girl from Mississippi named Laura Jones. Harriet lit up like fireworks on the Fourth of July.

She hugged him and started to do a little dance and said, "Amen! Hallelujah!" They danced around hugging and giving praises to God. When they settled back down Harriet told William, "I knew that God had something special waiting for you. You just had to wait on it."

"Hmm, from Mississippi, you say. Well, I know you're going to eat well, but you going to have to deal with one real problem. Black folks' memories in Auburn have gotten really short, just like those Israelites in the Bible. They have the nerve to frown at and turn their nose up at Blacks coming here from the South after the Civil War. Quickly forgetting that outside of your family and a few I can count on one hand they all came from the South. I know because I brought them here from the South. Now they're beginning to think they are better than others. You and Laura will be treated wrong by those people still trying to figure out who God is in their lives, but I know you will pass this test that the Lord will be giving you. Lord knows I can't wait to meet her!" They hugged and shared a moment of departure with William ready to take and cherish the young lady who would be his wife soon, Laura Jones.

When Mr. and Mrs. William Freeman settled into their married life in Auburn, New York, it wasn't very long before the verbal sniping and other mean activities commenced against Laura Freeman. Attempting to correct her diction was one of their favorite darts that they would throw at Laura because of her southern accent. At every opportunity there were individuals making sly remarks about her southern cuisine. They didn't leave William out of their rants. These same mean individuals were quick to make sure that Laura was constantly reminded that she had married one of those "crazy Freemans" whose crazy cousin killed all those people.

Laura and William turned their insult into a bounty of blessings by loving in spite of what was being presented to them. That bounty translated into the Freemans buying additional properties to expand on what Harry, Kate, Luke, Catherine, Platt, Mary, and his uncles, aunts, and cousins had purchased; all because William and Laura responded to their hate and meanness with love they only could obtain through the teachings of Jesus Christ.

The bounty permitted them to bring their own children into the world. Bessie, Elizabeth, Claude, Horace, Amy, Phoebe, Daniel, Bertha, Wheeler, and William were born in the Freeman home. A home that Laura and William bought in the exclusive east end of Auburn which was all white till the Freemans moved into 19 Foote Street. They had traded in mean innuendoes for outright racial hate being the first African Americans to live there.

One evening, Laura Freeman was awakened by someone banging on their front door. Laura's first inclination was that it was some neighborhood bullies attempting to disrupt their peace, but the knocks were hard and obsessive. Laura decided to let William handle this apparent need to garner their attention. As William opened the door, he saw a jittery young boy looking all around as he steadily continued to knock. William understood the boy's reason for being jittery; it was never safe for a person of color to be caught in the eastside of Auburn after dark. The boy looked up at William and said, "Miss Harriet's house is on fire!"

William ran back upstairs and told Laura what had happened, got dressed, and departed immediately to Harriet's home on South Street outside the city. When they arrived, the house was gone. Nothing remained of Harriet's house as she stood there in the night air being comforted by Nelson. When she noticed William approaching, she turned to go meet him. They embraced and she said, "Well, William, I guess the Lord has something better planned for us."

William assured her that he was there to be of whatever assistance she might need. Harriet told him that her only concern was for Nelson. She intimated to William that Nelson's ailment was getting worse and felt that staying around that foul air from the fire would make him sicker. William told her not to worry, that Nelson could stay with him and Laura for as long as necessary.

William and Laura were beginning to worry about Nelson's and Harriet's health. Harriet was beginning to slow down and wasn't able to bounce back from those familiar aches and pains. The Freemans thought that her posture was changing also. She was looking shorter than her normal five feet in height. Nelson, the strapping young man who with his fellow soldiers pulled a hospital train over fifty miles by hand, was now an emaciated shell suffering from tuberculosis. Consumption, as it was called, had made it impossible for Nelson to be an active participant in Harriet's work and the maintenance of the family.

William and Laura had engaged in several conversations about Harriet's and Nelson's health and well-being; and it would not be too long before the collision of "what was" and "what is" would become clearly defined. In order to maintain, Harriet had established a large pig farm on her property.

Harriet was still being denied her pension from the Civil War but was determined to make her mission for God a success by any means necessary. She would travel house to house throughout Auburn collecting garbage to turn into slop for her pigs. William would fuss with her about subjecting herself to the trials and tribulations of pig farming at her age. This was a task that neither Harriet nor William had any experience with. Sure, everyone knew how to tend and slaughter a few hogs, but Harriet had over two hundred. Visiting Harriet could be a trying affair if the wind was wafting in the wrong direction. Disaster hit in the middle of the summer when about forty of Harriet's pigs just dropped dead. This sent panic through the Tubman home. Harriet even got William and Laura involved.

Laura had been talking to a neighbor about the article she had read about Harriet's pigs dying. She told Laura, "That's a tragic shame about Harriet's pigs. She's such a nice lady. I hope that rat poison that I swept up in the garbage didn't contribute to her loss. I'm going to have to remember not to put that stuff in the garbage I set aside for Harriet."

When William arrived home that evening, she shared her conversation with the neighbor and provided him with her insight into what had killed Harriet's pigs. "It was clear that people were sweeping their floors and placing the debris from the floor into the same garbage they were giving to Harriet for her pigs. The sweepings could contain poisons and other things that would kill a human, let alone a hog," she exclaimed with great relief as she gave thanks to God for the clarity.

Laura was so grateful for the insight because her husband William J. Freeman, who was known in some circles by his nickname "Roundtree," was a man with a "steely resolve." It was apparent that this was passed down through every generation of Freemans from his grandparents Harry and Kate Freeman.

William could turn a perceived mole hill into an anticipated mountain and be prepared to handle any challenge it might provide. His unwritten anthem was, "The best way to kill a flea is with an axe." Unfortunately, in too many situations it was that kind of resolve that had gotten too many of William's family members in trouble in the past and currently. Laura would tell her husband over and over, "Resolve without God is like a horse pulling a heavy load down Camillus Hill without a driver. Sooner or later that horse is going to get run over by its own load." Laura had a right to be concerned; William did a pretty good job of maintaining a "true North" heading on his "life compass" with her guidance, but when a family member or an extremely close friend had been wronged, then all bets were off. His resolve would lose its driver, God.

William was beginning to surmise that the sudden loss of so many of Harriet's pigs was a contrived hateful event initiated to hurt Harriet's wellbeing. William was beginning to conjure up the stories his father Platt Freeman would tell him about his father Harry Freeman's "Tree Leopards." Laura's information was like a breath of fresh air and helped him to get his "Life Compass" back to finding "True North."

The task before William was helping Harriet to realize that, as the "Moses of her people," there were easier and less strenuous ways to bring God's mission to completion. Nelson's condition was worsening, and he knew that Harriet did not want to leave him. Her own health and strength were ebbing, but when you're on a "Mission for God," nothing takes precedence over it. He also realized that he was going to spend more of his free time helping his Auntie with her affairs.

Sarah Bradford had reissued the book about Harriet, and Harriet hoped it would bring her the kind of money needed to take care of the people God was sending to her. Even with Nelson getting weaker, Harriet was going to have to get on the speaking and convention circuit.

21

IT'S WRONG; BUT IT MAKES SENSE

The Civil War had concluded, Reconstruction had ended, and the country was in the midst of combining a "De Jure Facto Discrimination Policy" to address the laws and mores of our country with a "De Facto Discrimination Policy" to address the social edicts and folkways of our country, so that they could make segregation complete and acceptable to the white populous, thereby ushering in the "Era of Conciliatory Reunification."

All these activities were "wrong" according to God and the teachings of Jesus the Christ, but it made "sense" to the greed, avarice, fear, hatred, and envy promulgated by the devil's domain the world.

A "De Jure Facto Discrimination Policy" (Black Codes) permitted the institution of written laws on the federal level, state level, and local level upholding the "mores" and "wishes" of both north and south white Americans. Laws proclaiming, "Separate but Equal." A

"De Facto Discrimination Policy" (Jim Crow Laws) assured the denial of all Civil Rights to African Americans. This was accomplished by upholding the "folkways" and "social whims" of both north and south white Americans. These were ways that proclaimed there must be a divide. (*If there is a "Division Street in your town or a railroad track running through your town, they were the demarcation lines for the races of people. Henceforth the remark, "the wrong side of the tracks." The Author)

"Conciliatory Reunification" required mitigating the "wrongs" of slavery. This was being accomplished by the nation speaking less harshly about the impact of slavery on African Americans, developing approaches that could replace the economic opportunities of slavery such as sharecropping, use of the penal system for unrestricted free labor, and the use of mores and folkways to diminish and control the issue of equality with white Americans.

The Black Codes presented but were not limited to such laws as:

Blacks must have written Evidence of Employment, a labor contract, for the coming year in January. The absence of one was punishable by arrest and forced labor.

It was unlawful to have an occupation other than a farmer or servant unless you paid a tax between ten dollars and one hundred dollars.

Antienticement Laws punished anyone who offered higher wages to a black laborer already under contract.

Breaking a labor contract made blacks subject to arrest, beatings, and forced labor.

Apprenticeship Laws forced many minors to work for little or nothing if they were either orphans or whose parents were deemed unable to support them by a judge.

(Remember, particularly in the South, these officials were all ex-confederate soldiers or sympathizers who longed for the "good ole days." The Author)

Jim Crow has a national concept of laws. Some, but not all, of its components are presented here:

You must own property before you could vote in some Northern States.

The acceptance and promotion of the Ku Klux Klan.

Schools and Neighborhoods are segregated

"White Only" placards either specifically designated or implied were the dominate currency for the promotion of pure hatred in both the North and the South. The denominations of this currency of hatred ranged from the steps of God's Churches to the outhouses in the field.

Black Codes handled the "Mores" and Jim Crow handled the "Folkways."

(The reason James Crow can continue to impact our society "today" is solely based on Americans' inability to confront the issue without qualifiers. Americans are very uncomfortable confronting a "wrong moment." They don't want to admit that all components and people engaged in slavery were wrong and anything associated with the practice of slavery is wrong and we will not function in that way again, according to our beliefs in God. What they prefer to do is to identify a "make sense moment" to justify a "Wrong... but," and that permits dilution and "convenient amnesia." This is why James Crow is a more sophisticated and subtle prodigy of Jim Crow. The Author)

This was the world that William and Laura Freeman, along with Harriet Tubman, Nelson Davis, and every other African American, found themselves thrusted into. William longed for the days when men like his Father Platt Freeman, William Seward, his Uncle Luke Freeman, Abraham Lincoln, and Daniel Hughes "said what they meant and meant what they said" no matter what the cost. He racked his mind as to how could men lose so easily the friendship and trust that his father told him existed between his grandparents and John Hardenbergh.

As was his custom, William sought clarity from the Lord and received it. "The further people move away from my direction for their lives, the closer they embrace destruction by sin, lust, and envy of this world.

It had been twenty-five years since the end of the Civil War, and Harriet was still peddling her produce from a basket on her arm waiting for her pension from the Civil War. Her husband, Nelson Davis, had succumbed to tuberculosis, and she was earnestly trying to rekindle interest in the "Moses of her People" to fulfill her mission work for God while her health was fading.

William and Laura were facing the challenges of raising a large family in a hostile environment. Yes, the Freemans were a good family worthy of being recognized and followed by the local newspaper. Yes, William's work and relationship with the Seward family was well publicized. William and Laura Freeman's only angst was they were "uppity negroes" who didn't know how to "stay in their place." "What makes them think they belong or are wanted on Foote Street?" or "What makes them think they're better than me living up there on Foote Street when they own all this property down here? They just trying to be "uppity negroes."

"William, there are good, caring people out there both black and white that abhor the things happening to Harriet and treat us with respect and love and don't begrudge us living up on the Eastside of Auburn." Laura would attest to often when she would see that "LOOK" would build in his expression.

The "LOOK" was haughty and intimidating at the same time. It was like he was looking straight through you as if you weren't even there. According to some kinfolks, he got it honestly from his daddy and his daddy's daddy. They told Laura that when one of those Freeman boys took on that persona somebody could be in immediate danger.

Hearing of the "LOOK" made Laura chuckle and remember, "Well, I've seen William get that "LOOK," but he was raised right. He knows better than look the "LOOK" towards me. But his boys, that was another story. I was getting ready to have some friends over to the house that evening. It was a bright summer morning, and I noticed the woodwork in the parlor had several scuff marks from the kids playing in there when I wasn't around. Our oldest boy Wheeler came bouncing out of his bedroom heading to rush out and start a day of play and fun when I caught him with my famous motherly cry, "'Wheeler!'"

"What, ma?" came a stressful retort from young Wheeler Freeman.

"I need you to get a bucket, brush, and rag and wash the woodwork in the parlor before you go out to play," instructed his mother. "I have company coming over this evening, and I want those scuff marks gone!"

"But, Ma, my friends are waiting for me! Can I do it later this afternoon? I promise I'll do it before your company gets here," begged her son.

With a stern appearance and tired of discussing this matter with a child Laura said, "I don't give a 'cripple crab' about your friends waiting for you. Get that bucket, brush, and rag and get that woodwork done, NOW!"

Wheeler spun around and attempted to emulate his father with the "LOOK." Laura moved as quick as a cat and slapped the "LOOK" off his face and the "taste out of his mouth." That was the last time anyone in the Freeman household attempted the "LOOK" with Laura Freeman.

While the Freeman household was free of the "LOOK," society wasn't, and that is what scared Laura. William could become a very volatile man if the "LOOK" was permitted to ferment.

Society's inability to do right with Harriet Tubman. The harassment his family was encountering because people resented the Freemans for living in a white neighborhood. The "wrong" that Society was trying to make right through this "Conciliatory Reunification." All of it was weighing heavy on her husband.

"There's good people, both black and white, who feel just like you do," Laura reiterated.

"I know, but why don't they stand up and stop this madness?" William responded.

"For the same reason you're so upset. They haven't taken it to the Lord, and they're trying to figure it out the best they can by themselves just like you," Laura said.

William stopped dead in his tracks and realized that his consternation was all because he had not taken it to the Lord. He hugged his wife, thanked her for her guidance, and headed for the stairs of the back porch. William laid out his concerns and problems to the Lord and just meditated on all the Lord had brought him through until God brought him the clarity he needed to go forward.

When he reentered the house, he gave Laura a hug and thanked her for her guidance and love. William told her that the Lord made it clear that he was interfering with God's work.

"I've been too concerned about too many things," William confided to Laura. "God wants us to address the issues that he has given us directly. I have been consumed by the ills of the world. Our job is to be of service to those that God has given us."

"Well, dear," Laura said tenderly, "that would mean we have to devote more time to assisting Aunt Harriet with her mission for the Lord, checking more frequently to make sure Miss Matilda is alright, and be ready to provide God's services to anybody else God might send our way."

"Miss Matilda!" exclaimed William, "Haven't seen her in a month of Sundays. I'll pay her a visit tomorrow."

What William didn't know was the Lord had already told Laura what they were supposed to do but instructed her "To stay quiet and be patient until I have prepared your husband for acceptance of your task on the scale that I want."

William's involvement with the Sewards for well over forty years had given him a more worldly view than most Auburnians had acquired. It led him to desire to correct and improve concerns on a national and international level. However, the Lord needed him to take care of and support a couple of committed and dedicated sheep right in William's backyard right here in Auburn.

He knew what he had to do with Auntie Harriet. He was going to have to get more "hands on" with the maintenance of her property and wherever else he may be needed. He wasn't sure how he was supposed to support Miss Matilda, but he had promised the Lord to be more vigilant considering Miss Matilda.

Miss Matilda Hicks had been a part of Harry and Kate's free slave colony of New Guinea since William had a memory. She had been abused as a sex slave by her master until she was able to escape on a trip to Baltimore from his plantation in Virginia. When she finally reached Auburn and the safety of New Guinea, she spent her first week at the Praise House at New Guinea giving God praise and worship for her freedom from bondage. She would tell the Lord, "Lord, freedom taste so good!" over and over and over. Everywhere she would go on the New Guinea property she could be seen smiling and saying, "Freedom taste so good.... Freedom taste so good!"

As was the custom on slaveholding plantations, the young female or females who were going to satisfy the sexual appetites of the plantation owners of the "main house" were never field slaves. They were always house slaves whose primary duties centered around the kitchen. Matilda was no exception to this rule, and she learned to become a great chef of a variety of culinary delights and international wonders. She realized that being over occupied in the kitchen could reduce the time she had to spend being abused in the master's bed.

Mary and Platt wanted her to get exposure and gain recognition for her culinary skills in the Auburn area, but Matilda refused. She was so scared of being recaptured and sent back to her master's plantation that she would not leave New Guinea in the light or shadows of day. Mary decided that Matilda would become part of New Guinea's educational process. She would set up classes to teach women and young girls how to cook. Matilda also planted a garden to produce fresh herbs of all sort and dried and store the herbs, so that winter cooking was never bland, but she would not venture outside of New Guinea. There were several residents of New Guinea who possessed the same fear that Matilda had about being recaptured. Platt, like his father Harry before him, would assign these folks tasks around New Guinea for its upkeep and maintenance.

This continued until President Lincoln announced the 13th Amendment freeing all slaves in the South. This was the clarion call that freed Matilda and her other compadres who were terrified of recapture and being returned to slavery.

Matilda was now free to share culinary skills and epicurean delights with the Auburn community. As with all the free Blacks and runaway Blacks, it was always more prudent to keep your actual truth to yourself. Matilda kept her truth to herself and would inform the inquisitive that she arrived North shortly after gaining her freedom from the 13th Amendment. Matilda truly believed in that Bible quote, "Be as wise as a serpent and as harmless as a dove."

Over the decades she had gained a major reputation as a great cook, but now she was getting older and was beginning to ail. On occasions, Miss Matilda had stayed with William and Laura for extended periods to recuperate, but they hadn't talked with her or seen her in a couple of months. William would rectify this tomorrow.

It was raining and very damp when William and Laura arrived at Matilda's house. Laura had decided, through God's prodding, to accompany William to Matilda's home. Matilda was a very proud woman, and if it had been William rapping at her door she would have never opened it, but she heard Laura's voice saying, "Miss Matilda, Miss Matilda, it's Laura Freeman. I just stopped by to see how you were doing."

The door creeped open, and there was Miss Matilda looking gaunt and ill. Laura motioned to William to stay on the porch as she went in. Miss Matilda's steps were measured, and her voice had a shaky trill. As they went to sit down, Laura could see in the kitchen sink a watermelon with its top cut off and a spoon sticking in it.

Laura knew exactly what that meant. Miss Matilda was too sick to cook for herself, so every now and then she would get a few spoonsful of watermelon to sustain her existence.

"How long have you been ill, Miss Matilda?" Laura inquired with great care and concern.

"Oh, about three weeks, but I'm getting better," she said trying to deflect concern.

"Miss Matilda, you know William and I are concerned about you, and I'm not going to sit here and lollygag with you when loving action is needed," Laura stated with all the authority God had given her to rectify this situation. "William is outside on the porch. We're going to gather your things, and you are going to move in with us. Besides, after we get you all healed up, with those children of mine I need all the help I can get. Those boys are something else."

Miss Matilda, with a tear of joy and gratitude to God for answering her plea for help, rose from the chair and started to guide Laura in the gathering of her belongings. When Laura and Miss Matilda opened the door they saw William in the corner of the porch rocking and praying. Laura asked him, "What are you doing, sweetheart?"

"Well, when you went inside the Lord told me to hold your arms up like Aaron and Hur did for Moses, so that was what I was doing," he said with a smile of obedience and accomplishment.

Miss Matilda became part of the Freeman household for the rest of her life, and her presence was a true blessing to everyone in William and Laura's home. William's brother Thomas fell on hard times, and he also became part of Laura's and William's homestead. They had also purchased 17 Foote St., and the additional room was greatly appreciated. Auntie Harriet would tease William about starting Tubman House number two on the eastside of town. "How you think your neighbors are going to like that?" She would giggle.

"Auntie, I don't give a 'crippled crab' what they think!" William replied with his own giggle that turned into a back-bending belly laugh for both of them. William had learnt the "crippled crab" saying from his wife

Laura and found out it was helping him with his cussing problem.

William had become more "hands on" around Harriet's property. Unofficially, William was literally managing the Tubman property. Every component of life on Harriet's Estate had Freeman involvement. Laura had gotten involved in the pragmatic needs of the old soldiers and people of need who resided in Harriet's Hospital Home. She would address some of the practical needs of the Home and served as a major liaison between the Thompson AME Zion Church and the Home.

Harriet was off the speaking circuit and out of the public eye and its remembrance. To the general population of Auburn, she was the vegetable peddling street vendor who did something with slaves during the Civil War. Her sacrifices and heroics had faded in the memories of the country she worked hard to build, but her commitment and resolve to fulfill her mission assigned to her by God had not waned. Given her health challenges and the need for resources for the Home, Harriet had turned more and more to "Mother Zion."

The Auburn component of "Mother Zion" was the Thompson Memorial AME Zion Church. It had recently moved into its new edifice on Parker Street and was an important nucleus to the African American population of Auburn. In spite of her struggles, Harriet Tubman-Davis was deeply committed to the wellbeing and success of Thompson Memorial. The Freemans and other families were just as deeply committed to the success of the church, and this consortium of togetherness had begun to address issues of pertinent concern to the African American community in Auburn.

Harriet and William began to seek out the church's involvement in the work of the Home both in construction activities and upkeep initially. Operation on a day-to-day basis was improving because of William. He had reduced Harriet's dependency on raising pigs. He had reduced the herd of pigs to a manageable number that was only being maintained to provide food to the Home and Harriet's household.

The tremendous loss of livestock years ago was due to the garbage Harriet had been collecting to create slop for feed. Harriet's need to collect garbage throughout Auburn was only necessitated because of her feed-crops being ruined over and over by birds. They were not natural flocks of birds passing through, but farmed-raised pigeons. Domesticated pigeons being raised on the Metcalf Farm north of Harriet's property by Mrs. Butler were totally decimating Harriet feedstock, eating corn and vegetables.

William had made several visits to the Metcalf Farm to seek relief and assistance to bring this destruction to an end. His reception by Mrs. Butler and others at the farm was cold and dismissive. William justified in his mind that more stringent actions must be taken given the damage those pigeons were doing to Harriet's crops.

When William confided in Laura what his plan for remedying the situation entailed, Laura was greatly upset.

"William, two wrongs don't make a right! How do you expect God to continue to bless us if you are going to run around here like you don't know Him?" Laura pleaded with him.

William was moving away from his wife like she was throwing hot coals at him and said, "I got to do what I got to do!" and he walked out the door.

William Freeman was not doing a good job at handling the "tests of patience" that God was placing before him. He had the situation at home where neighborhood kids were bullying his boys. He had gone to Recorder Kent's office to lodge an official complaint, informing them if something wasn't done, he would take matters into his own hand. The only thing that transpired was a small article in the Auburn Bulletin mitigating the situation with the title "But Boys Will Be Boys."

On the corner of East Genesee and Owasco Streets an out-of-control bicyclist coming down the Owasco Street hill ran over him and left him dazed with a bad gash in the back of his head. The bicyclist went sprawling. After the bicyclist gathered himself, he looked at William muttered something that William couldn't understand in his dazed condition, and rode off. Thank

God Doctor Austin was nearby to render assistance. Others were just looking on.

It was difficult for him to have a birthday party in peace. Two drunk fellows, Lewis Johnson and Richard Wood, barged their way into the Freeman home and were thrown out the house into the streets where a fight broke out bringing the attention of Officer Birdsall.

William's most pressing concern and most worrisome challenge was his children. This centered around his boys in particular. They were developing a similar temperament of entitlement similar to several of their uncles. They had no interest in how the Freemans prospered through devotion to God and hard work. They thought they were entitled to all the benefits and awards of just being a Freeman. He even had to call the police on his son Wheeler for stealing from his Uncle Thomas who was staying in William's home. On and on William was finding himself in contentious situations that made peace difficult for him to attain, and his visitations with God were slipping his mind more frequently than before.

His resolve was waning. He felt that direct action was needed on his part concerning Harriet's wellbeing. He rationalized, even though he knew better, that God was silent because the Lord was waiting on him to take the lead and do something.

William had gone back to Harriet's homestead and began mixing strychnine into some corn and seeds. He was determined to rectify this situation on his own. He spread his toxic mixture in close proximity to the flock of pigeons that were inundating the Tubman-Davis property. It wasn't long before William's desired outcome was in effect. The pigeons were dying.

William was quite pleased with his intervention until he was paid a visit by State Game Protector Willard A. Hoagland serving him a warrant for his arrest by Acting Recorder Ben Kenyon. The arrest warrant was for having "corn poisoned with strychnine scattered about the lot north of the Harriet Tubman Home in South Street which Freeman is alleged to be working."

Well, like everything else that occurred to the William and Laura Freeman Family, it became newsworthy for the *Auburn Citizen* on Saturday, May 18, 1907.

William J. Freeman was totally embarrassed as he sat in a jail cell waiting for Laura to bail him out. Not because it was the first time in his life he had been incarcerated, nor because he had armed his detractors with "live ammunition" to belittle his name and reputation, but because of the embarrassment and ridicule Laura and his family would have to endure. It was especially upsetting at a time when he was trying to set a "Godly Example" for his boys.

That was it in a nutshell. How are you supposed to set a "Godly Example" when you haven't sought a "Godly

Advice"? He had been too long away from his first love, God, by leaning on his own understanding. God didn't need William's help in addressing what appeared to be a dire situation. William realized he was acting just like the Israelites in the book of Judges, "In those days Israel had no king; all the people did whatever seemed right in their own eyes." (Judges 21:25, NLT)

William asked the Lord for forgiveness and vowed never to lean on his own understanding again! He decided that from now on he would wait on the Lord.

22

HOPE SPRINGS ETERNAL

William's brief sortie into the life of incarceration was all he needed to reset his spiritual compass back to True North and a complete dependency on God. He finally accepted those things God gave him directly to address and left everything else in the Lord's Hands. William had to learn to leave God's business to God. His exposure to man's inhumanity to man had made him a "warrior of justice" in his mind. He was trying to right every wrong and correct every injustice just because God allowed him to be made aware of "God Concerns." What God wanted from William was prayer, not opinions, obedience, not action.

While he was busy being unfocused on what God had laid directly in front of him to address, his sons were out of control. William had taken for granted his children of privilege. They didn't have to work as he did nor his father did as a child. Laura and he had worked extremely hard to give their children opportunities that were not afforded to them. Their daughters were more judicious in the combining of what they "should do" with what they "wanted to do," but not the boys.

The boys were another question. They were gifted with the historical "Freeman giftings" that were a common trait since Harry and Kate Freeman, but they were not being employed in the traditional manner. Those sacred skills given to them by God for "His Purpose" were being misused and misapplied because the boys put their entire emphasis on "what they want to do," regardless of the mandates of God. They felt entitled to "cut across the grass" without abiding by prescribed regulations. They wanted to be the boss of whatever they were doing without following the path to become a leader. They were frustrated, and there was nothing their father could do for them but pray. They had placed the teachings that their parents had shared and attempted to embed in them about Christ on the shelf. The only exception was Claude, whose condition and circumstances were different from the other boys which allowed him to have the stability to go forward and succeed. William knew the power of prayer and wasn't going to concede failure as it related to his sons.

His family wasn't the only concern God had assigned to him. He told Laura, "Baby, God has given me too much on my plate to do!"

Laura smiled and said lovingly, "Dear, when you take time to listen to the Lord, he'll give you a platter to re-place your plate to handle whatever He wants done."

Once again William found himself realizing that only the Lord could give him what he needed to be effective in addressing this avalanche of concerns encompassing his life.

His Auntie wasn't doing good, and Miss Matilda was not doing well either. The two women who had meant so much to their growth as human beings looked like they were preparing themselves for their trip home to the Lord.

William and Laura were finding themselves spending more and more time with Aunt Harriet. It was not only just related to work and care of the estate but just to be with her. Mrs. Griger and the other ladies took great care of Harriet around the clock. They had convinced her to take up residency in the Home to assure that she and the residents of the Home could have proper care with their limited staff. Harriet had confided in William that she was going to turn her entire mission for God over to Mother Zion. "It's the only way I can make sure this work for God continues," Harriet explained to him. "Son, you won't abandon my mission, will you?" she asked al-ready knowing the answer.

"No, Auntie, I won't abandon your mission for God," he reassured her.

Laura and William had always been involved in the affairs of the Thompson Memorial AME Zion Church. They realized how the tiny praise house at New Guinea had planted the seed to allow Mother Zion to initiate the Thompson Memorial AME Zion Church in Auburn, New York. The Freemans historically had been major contributors and always accepted prominent positions and responsibility since the days of his father Platt and his Uncle Luke. Now their role with the church would take on added significance with Auntie relinquishing control of the Home and the entire estate. Their role in Harriet's mission for God had just been magnified with that revelation.

Transitioning to church control was not a complicated process due to the fact that she was dealing with like-minded people. They were people who loved the Lord like she did, and those people were her fellow members of Thompson Memorial and Mother Zion. The only thing left to do was make it official and establish the proper organizational structure.

The Western New York Council of the AME Zion Church took over direct responsibility for the Home, Harriet's private house and all additional property. The Council also accepted the day-to-day care of Harriet Tubman-Davis. They setup a trustee board that would address management issues of the property. For the day-to-day care of Harriet and the Home, a lady managers board was established. William and Laura Freeman became integral parts of both the trustee board and the lady managers board, respectively.

In order to solidify this new relationship between the Harriet Tubman-Davis estate and Mother Zion, it was necessary to make it the major focus of Western New York Conference of the A.M.E. Zion Churches.

Here is the local accounting:

THE AUBURN CITIZEN, SATURDAY, JUNE 11, 1910

THE TUBMAN HOME
Reports Show Accomplishments of the Year.

FREEMAN TO WORK LAND
And Pay the Home $100 a Year for the Privilege—

A Financial Statement

"The sixty-first session of the of the Western New York Conference of A.M.E. Zion church met at Ithaca on June 1 and closed Monday evening June 6. Bishop C.R. Harris presided and was assisted by Bishop G.L. Blackwell of Phila-

delphia. The delegate from the Auburn church was Mrs. H.T. Johnson. Mrs. E.U.A. Brooks is the president of the Varick C.E. Society and presided at the annual meeting on Friday evening, June 3. Rev. Mr. Brooks was elected secretary of the conference and complier of its minutes.

The appointments for the ensuing year are as follows: Presiding elder, T.A. Aiuten; Rochester and Canandaigua, J.W. Brown; Auburn, E.U.A. Brooks; Ithaca, C.L. Harris; Syracuse, E.S. Bailey; Watertown, N.C. Rountree; Gloversville and Johnstown, W.B. Caines; Saratoga, H.J. Starks; Schenectady, S.W. Hutchings; Schoharie, J.H. Taylor; Wilkesbarre and Montrose, C. Campbell; Binghamton, J.C. Roberts; Waverly, Towanda and Corning, J.C. Walters; Elmira, J.H Ellison; Norwich and Oneida, G.H. Morse; Amsterdam, G.C. Smith; Jamestown, to be supplied. Transferred to the New

York Conference, J.W.H. Johnson, Missionaries: C.A. Smith, E.J. Butler and W.H. Denslow Supernumeraries: W.B. Brown, D.A. Johnson, W.L. Lane, J.C. Parola. The conference will convene next year at Saratoga on June 14.

The annual joint session of the trustees and lady managers of the Harriet Tubman Home convened in the A.M.E. Zion church of this city [Auburn] on Tuesday, June 7, with the president, Bishop C.R. Harris in the chair. The report of Mrs. James Dale, treasurer of the board of lady managers, showed that during the year she had received $358.85, expended $321.42 and had left in the treasury $37.43. The report of James Dale, treasurer of the local board of trustees, showed that he had received $277.07 during the year, expended $266.88 and had on hand $10.19. Mrs. S. Griger, matron of the Home, has on hand $91 for the erection of a porch at *the Home.*

Rev. E.U.A. Brooks, the secretary and special financial agent of the Home, reported that he had received from the various churches of the Western New York Conference during the year $186.93 to which 10 cents was added at the meeting, making the amount $187.03 in that fund. The Home now owns 17 small and four large pigs.

The election of Mrs. Griger as matron and William Freeman as superintendent were ratified. The total amount received by the Treasurers of the two boards was $635.92. Rev. Brooks received this year from the churches $101.10. During the year Mrs. Griger raised $40, and donated $30.48 more for moving expenses and improvement. Grand total of receipts $807.50. Expenses of trustee board covering coal, repairs, live stock and food for the same $266.88. Expenses of board *of lady managers covering the salary of matron, provisions, clothing and other provisions $321.42. Expenses and repairs paid by Mrs. Griger, #30.48, grand total of expenses, $618.78. Total balances in hand from this year's receipts, $188.62. Cash on hand from last year $112.93, making a grand total cash on hand in all treasuries of $301.55.*

Rev. J.C. Parola was elected general agent. Rev. E.U.A. Brooks was elected secretary and special financial agent. The officers of the local trustee and lady managers' boards were re-elected. The superintendent, William Freeman, has agreed to work the land for two years and will pay the Home $100 per year for the privilege. He will also care for the pigs belonging to the institution and have supervision of the Home property, except the brick cottage and the land enclosed about it."

THE POST-STANDARD, SYRACUSE, N.Y., FRIDAY

FUNDS ARE MUCH NEEDED

To Carry on the Laudable Work of the Tubman House

"Among the Inmates of the Harriet Tubman Home, according to the annual report of the officers of the institution, is one who has attained the extreme age of 113 years. There are also many others of advance age who are benefitting by the good work instituted by Aunt Harriet and no person in the Home is below 60 years. At present the managers of the institution are in pressing need of funds and all contributions will be gratefully received.

The officials of the Home are- Trustees: Rev. G.L. Blackwell, presiding Bishop of Philadelphia; Rev. James E. Mason, Bishop Rochester; Rev J.H. McMullen, Rochester, Rev R. Farley Fisher,

Bishop, Ithaca; Rev L.I. Wood, Bishop, Elmira; Rev S. Bailey, Syracuse; Rev J.C. Roberts, Presiding Elder, Binghamton; Rev C.A. Smith, Auburn; Rev P.K. Fonvielle, Auburn; Mr. H.T. Johnson, Auburn; Mr. William Freeman, Auburn; Rev. E.U.A. Brooks, General Superintendent, Saratoga; Board of Managers. Mrs. C.G. Cannon, president; Mrs. Elmer Cooper, vice president; Mrs. C.S. Mathews, recording secretary; Mrs. James Dale, treasurer; Mrs. C.A. Smith, matron; Mrs. H.T. Johnson corresponding secretary; Mrs. L Stanton, Mrs. Francis Brown, Mrs. Emma Nelson and Mrs. Laura Freeman, all of Auburn; Mrs. E.U.A. Brooks, Saratoga; Mrs. Sarah Ross, Syracuse; Mrs. Sarah Ross, Syracuse; Mrs. F.R. Ridgeway, Mrs. Sarah Reid and Mrs. F. Johnson, Elmira; Mrs. R. Hawkins, Geneva; Mrs. Ella Belcher, Ithaca."

Before the meetings, William had worried Laura

about every possible scenario that could arise that could negatively impact Auntie's property. His major concern was having to expend resources to pay someone to manage her property. William had no problems with paying a matron and support staff given Harriet's age and circumstances. All the residents were elderly with the ages of the occupants of the Home, with the oldest being 113 years old and the youngest being 63 years old.

"Those folks are old!" exclaimed William with a profound look of worry. "That's going to really tax what little resources we have to get through the year, and put on top of that cost to pay a superintendent. What if he starts making bad decisions, or what if he starts using Auntie's resources to profit himself? A cad like that could ruin everything that Auntie has worked for! I'm not going to sit back and allow anybody to destroy what she has accomplished. Before I let that happens, I'll..."

Laura, weary of all the doomsday talk, stopped him in mid-sentence and said, "Why don't you pay to be the superintendent? Then you won't have to worry about somebody else being elected to the position and doing the wrong thing."

"William, you're missing the entire point," she continued. "Everything Auntie has ever done in her life was with the blessing and protection of the Lord. She's crawled through the swamps, spent cold nights in the woods with a three-thousand-dollar bounty on her head time and time again just to bring people to freedom in the North. She didn't charge anybody for doing it nor did she ask for anything. The only thing she requested was what was due to her for her service to her country during the Civil War, her pension. Our government spent thirty years denying Aunt Harriet her pension. Did that stop her? Did that deter her from her 'Mission for God,' no. She did what was necessary to make her 'Mission for God' a reality. William Freeman, I know what it's like to have hounds chasing you and somebody control every moment of every day of your life. I know what it means to be a slave," she said with the sternness necessary to allow her message to sink into the battleground of her husband's mind and thoughts.

"Besides, honey, where you see age as a liability, I see it as a blessing," she quipped. "I was reading an article by Booker T. Washington. I wish he and W.E.B. Dubois would stop feuding about ideology and come together for the betterment of African Americans. Dubois is spearheading a new organization called the National Advancement for Color People, the NAACP. Not to be outdone, Washington is spearheading the start of a new organization called the National Urban League up in Niagara Falls this year. Oh my God, I've allowed the Devil to get me off track again by feeding my 'hot points' of concerns. I've got to stay focused on the task before me," Laura said, being glad that she caught herself and was back on track with the task given to her by God.

"William, did you know that the life expectancy for white America was forty-nine years for males and fifty-two years for females?" She had presented this fact as a rhetorical question to her husband not looking for a response from him. So, she continued, "That's what I was reading about in Booker T.'s article and was trying to address before I got sidetracked with their politics. Booker T. was explaining that the life expectancy of black Americans was eight to ten years less. Yes, William, forty-one years for a black male and forty-four years for a black female. William, it's nothing but God! Auntie has been true to her 'Mission for God,' and God has blessed them souls with long life."

William jumped up and started his little happy dance and spun Laura around kissed her and said, "My baby to the rescue again! That's just what I'm going to do. I'm going to pay one hundred dollars a year to be Auntie's superintendent!"

With no debate nor discussion, it was announced in the April meeting and confirmed at that June 1st to the 6th meeting that William Freeman would be the superintendent of the estate and would pay one hundred dollars a year for the privilege. William's contribution made up 27 percent of needed income ($358) to operate Harriet's Estate. William had resolved his most pressing issue in behalf of Auntie Harriet and her care, but he was about to enter a long season where the development of his faith with God would be the only thing that could keep his "hope alive."

Laura and William carried out their responsibilities to Harriet and the Home. Unfortunately, it was becoming clearer that Auntie was closer to obtaining her eternal reward. As Harriet was growing feebler and was sleeping longer and longer, all her family, the matron, and the Freemans could do was pray for her comfort and sing her favorite spirituals. As if on cue, Auntie woke up from her slumber and said, "I go to prepare a place for you." Aunt Harriet then turned her head, closed her eyes, and joined the angels around God's Throne. Harriet Tubman-Davis was called home by the Lord on March 10, 1913. Harriet Tubman-Davis had committed her life to carrying out the "Will of God." Well done, Auntie, well done. "The mission of the Home will continue."

Harriet was given a military funeral. Despite the cold, it was the largest funeral conducted at Fort Hill Cemetery since the funeral of William Seward. As William and Laura were preparing to attend Auntie's funeral, they heard a deep raspy cough coming from Miss Matilda's room. Laura responded to the sounds of distress by checking on her. Miss Matilda had insisted the night before that she was going to attend her old friend's funeral. It was apparent that Miss Matilda would be missing Harriet's funeral. William called for his daughter Amy and instructed her to "keep a close eye on Miss Matilda until we return."

When William and Laura returned home from Harriet's funeral, they found the doctor in with Matilda. He was sitting in her room as if he had been waiting for them to arrive home. Dr. Austin greeted Laura and William then stated, "Matilda has something to share with you that she should have shared some time earlier."

Everyone's attention turned to Miss Matilda as she pulled herself up on her pillows. Laura and William looked over to the corner where Amy was sitting. It was clear from her posture that whatever the news was it was not going to be good.

"You know I love you, and I'm truly grateful for what you have done for me over these last ten years." Miss Matilda was still resisting revealing her diagnosis, but Dr. Austin had explained to her that it was more of a disservice not to share, particularly since she hadn't finalized her earthly business. "I'm sick, children. Dr. Austin has been treating me for sugar and cancer for the last twelve years. Doc is telling me I don't have much time left, and what I have saved from working over sixty years, I want you to have it as a token of my love."

Dr. Austin saw Amy looking strange when Matilda mentioned "sugar" interjected quickly, "sugar" is a folk term for diabetes.

"We're not concerned about what you got in some bank.

Doc, is there anything we can do?" William proclaimed.

"No," said Dr. Austin, "Matilda and I have been combating these maladies for the last twelve years. It's only by the grace of God that we are sitting here having this conversation now. Ten years ago, it was appearing that she would not see Christmas."

"Enough talking about dying, I'm still alive!" was Matilda's pronouncement. She looked over at Amy and said, "Come here, baby."

Amy took a slow walk across the room and fell into Matilda's arms. Matilda put her arms around her and just rocked her back and forth as the adults left the room.

Miss Matilda Hicks had been living with the Freemans for the past ten years. She had been ailing for some time, but now with this revelation, it appeared they were advancing into the most critical stage, the end of life. Amy Freeman, the most responsible child of Laura and William, was extremely close to Miss Matilda.

Amy would read the Bible to her and listen to Miss Matilda's stories about life. The revelation of Matilda's life expectancy on the heels of Auntie's death and burial kept the Freemans on their knees. Now that her secret was out, Matilda got very serious about getting her business in order. One day she summoned Laura and William and told them how much she appreciated the love they had shown her all these years. She told them that they were the only family she ever had. Matilda shared with them the banks she had money deposited, but she couldn't find her saving books.

Now, William was leery about letting people into his business. He had suffered the impact of people's greed and meanness over the years. Whatever amount of money Miss Matilda had in those banks, he wanted to go and just retrieve it. He knew it was going to be difficult to get what little money Miss Matilda had in those banks without her bank books.

Amy and Laura found William's proposed approach to be unacceptable. They convinced him that there were serious ramifications from not using the proper protocol in this matter.

Amy explained, "Daddy, legal documentation is important to make sure Miss Matilda's money don't end up in the wrong hands. She must have a will written-up. Otherwise, anybody could claim that Miss Matilda said that they were to receive her money. Daddy, this would be catastrophic. The only ones who would receive Miss Matilda money would be lawyers fighting over it in court."

Amy's suggested direction for her father concerning Miss Matilda persuaded him to seek out a lawyer. William always had problems with the way lawyers could float on the currents no matter what the situation. He thought that being a lawyer was a sacred position. William thought all lawyers should be of the same caliber as William Seward. He knew that he was not going to find a lawyer like his old employer and friend. In the past, William had used Frank S. Corburn to transact his official business. So, he went to the office of attorney Frank S. Corburn asking him to visit Miss Matilda in order to create a will for her.

Frank Corburn visited the Freeman's home and established Matilda Hick's will.

Miss Matilda Hicks died on June 13, 1913. With will in hand, the exploration of Miss Hicks' assets began. To the astonishment of everyone involved, Miss Matilda had accumulated $10,327 worth of savings. This sum shocked the region; it made headlines in Auburn and Syracuse. To realize that a former slave could accumulate that large of a savings was so remarkable that the *Syracuse Herald*, thirty miles away, wrote a story about Miss Matilda's savings. As was the historical practice of reporting about African Americans, accuracy was not important.

SYRACUSE HERALD NEWSPAPER,
OCTOBER 16, 1913
FORMER SLAVE WHO DIED
IN AUBURN LEAVES $10,327

"An inventory of the estate of

*Martha Hix or Hicks, an aged col-
ored woman of Auburn, who died
last June shows that William
Freeman of Auburn is heir to
#10,327.11 which was found to be
on deposit in her name in various
banking houses in Auburn.*

*Maratha Hix was between 80 and
90 years old at the time of her
death. Her exact age is unknown.
In her youth she was a slave coming North to live after the civil
war. For many years she worked
as a domestic in various Auburn
families and was famous as a
cook, but as age came upon her
she gradually gave up her work,
living at times at the home of Mr.
and Mrs. William Freeman in
Foote street, and two years ago
coming to make it her permanent
home. She died June 20th leaving
a will which named William Freeman as her executor and heir,
though no mention of property
was made, nor did anyone suspect
that she had saved any money*

from her wages or otherwise pro-
vided for her old age. She had no
relatives in the world as far as
can be learned."

Turmoil surrounding Miss Matilda's will for the next two years kept William Freeman in the courts and the headlines as he battled Frank Corburn over his inequitable service fee.

THE AUBURN CITIZEN, THURSDAY,
JANUARY 21, 1915

COBURN CASE ON TRIAL IN JANUARY TERM
William Freeman,
Who charges Attorney With Charging

Exorbitant Fee, Tells Story—A Disagreement

"When he told me he was going to
charge me $3,000, I said, 'Mercy,
why don't you take it all?'..."

THE AUBURN CITIZEN JANUARY, 1915
THE CORBURN CASE
Will Go to the Jury Late This Afternoon
TRIAL WAS RATHER SPICY

Expert Hamilton Was One
of Several Witnesses for the Attorney

"Evidence in the case of William Freeman, (colored.) against County Attorney Frank S. Coburn, was concluded at 3:35 o'clock this afternoon after an interesting day in court..."

"William Freeman, sworn as the first witness said he was 73 years old and had long resided in Auburn. He had known the Matilda Hicks referred to for 25 years.

Witness showed temper when Mr. Corburn raised objections to Mr. Parker's questions as to Freeman's daughter advising him as to getting a will drawn, and was inclined to talk strongly and at random in spite of the court's wishes. He denied that he ever agreed to pay Corburn $3,000 for services in the matter, also that the first proposition to give him half what the estate would *amount to was refused..."*

"THE AUBURN CITIZEN, JANUARY 1915
JURY IN CORBURN CASE COULD NOT AGREE
One Man Said to Have Held Out Against a Verdict
for the Plaintiff—Will Be Moved for Trial in May"

The loss of Aunt Harriet and Miss Matilda, along with the turmoil of ongoing court proceedings with Frank Corburn, combined with male children functioning out of control palled in comparison to the blow William had to endure six weeks earlier in December of 1914. On December 10, 1914 Laura took her dancing place around God's Throne. She had taken ill in October and had died in December.

William was numb with loss. Laura was the rhythm of his life, and he had never considered a scenario without her. He had waited a long time before he had married and was "happy glad" that God had allowed him to be joined in life with his "Mississippi Miracle," and now she was gone. It was now when the Freeman Family Motto, "Endure and Achieve," took full effect in his life. William was numb; the "joy factor" no longer lived in his life. He "Endured" life and went through it numb for the rest of his life. He "Achieved" those goals that were necessary to raise his children and maintain his family. His life now took on a mechanical approach.

Life goes on no matter what tremor shakes your existence. The trial against Attorney Corburn was on his platter. This would be a major challenge he would have to face. This is what loomed and garnered his attention just six weeks after the death of his beloved Laura.

William still had children to raise and a life to live, so he grew more and more dependent on God's Understanding. His daily devotion was the only thing that gave him the strength to complete the cycle of a day, given his immediate challenges of family and court. To the outside world he appeared to be the same Mr. Freeman he had always been.

William Freeman had amassed a large portfolio of real estate by building upon what Harry and Kate Freeman had established over a hundred years ago in 1801. Envy and greed of some White and Black Auburnians had been the major opposition to the stability of the Freemans' real estate holdings, but year after year, the Freemans from the New Guinea Colony in Auburn prevailed. Their success was not by sending their children off to distinguished universities but an abiding devotion to serve God and realizing "God will make a way." This was immortalized by the saying over the door in every Freeman's home, *"Jesus Never Fails."*

William's relatives owned property all throughout Auburn adhering to their heritage. William Freeman himself owned massive amounts of properties throughout Auburn. Clearly William Freeman's vast holdings were starting to take a toll on the seventy-year-old patriarch. His real estate holdings included properties on Foote Street, N. Division Street, Fort Street, Bailey Street, Fitch Ave., all of Worden Lane, and most of Chapman Ave., east of Garrow Street. For forty-two years he had handled them mostly with the assistance and guidance of Laura J Freeman, but now he felt all alone. Not that he was physically alone his children, other relatives and strangers in need still resided with him. His loneliness sprouted from the death of Laura and the realization his children were developing their own independent personalities and were moving forward with their concept of a bright future. Be it right or be it wrong.

He had noticed that Amy and that Johnson boy, Percival, were spending more and more time conversing and grinning in each other's faces. This made him giggle inside because he could just imagine the conversations Amy would have had with her mother about Percival Johnson. He was sure Laura had told Amy, "Daddy is not ready for this kind of conversation..."

William chuckled to himself and began to think about his older baby girl, Bessie. Bessie and Amy were like two peas in a pod even though Bessie was ten years older than Amy. Bessie was a lot like Amy in personality and decorum. Bessie Freeman was the one that William knew had the skills and temperament to take over the Freeman Family business.

What William had not considered, while surmising Bessie's role in the continuation of the family business, was his independent spirit in her and "love." Bessie was a typical Freeman wanting to chart her own independent course regardless of the benefits and rewards of staying the defined family course. This created the "Clash of the Titans" between Bessie and her father. Laura would try to temper her husband's favorite dictum "Case Closed!" but neither of these two "rhino-skulled Freemans" would concede one inch of their point of view. The good thing was they would go to their designated corners in the same house at 19 Foote Street, mumble and sulk until the next family meal, be it breakfast, lunch, or dinner, and act like the "war of the universe" had not transpired earlier.

Enter one Joseph Walters. Bessie no longer had time to engage Daddy in those earth-shaking debates. She was in love. This became very disconcerting to William. While Laura would frantically try to teach him about the growth and development of a young lady, William remained elusive of any growth in this area. William treated it as if Laura was trying to teach him a language that he didn't need. It just didn't make sense to him.

"Okay, I get it!" he would tell Laura. "Bessie has just

as much right to be in love as we do. If she comes to me and says, 'Daddy, Joe and I want to get married,' Laura, I would give her and Joe my blessing and set him up in business so money would never be a problem."

"That's the problem!" Laura asserted. "They will want their own life together their own way. They don't want to live in the shadows of a big oak tree. They know they cannot get the light they want or think they want up under your massive Freeman Tree. We did not raise her in the shadows, and she's not going to live that way. Bessie loves Joe, and she will move with him to a place where the soil may not be as good as it is here, but the light will be better in their opinion."

Sure, enough Bessie married Joseph Walters and moved to Elmira, New York. Their relationship with Laura and William was great, but Elmira was on the other side of the world to William. He had learned his lesson with Bessie and started "trimming his tree limbs" with the help of Laura. She was great at reaching those limbs he couldn't get to. Laura had gone home to the Lord, so he knew he had to be very careful with Amy's budding romance with Percival Johnson. He wasn't going to make the same mistake again.

He thanked the Lord on the back porch's steps and spent the rest of the day just meditating and praising the Lord. William was happy that he could be corrected by Laura during her life. He praised the fact that God did not need to make him as stubborn as pharaoh by hardening his heart and making him not listen to him through Laura. William started doing his little "happy dance" for so long that the weak spot on the back porch was about to give way. William stopped his "happy dance," not because he wanted to, but his twenty-five-year-old mind was putting a whooping on his seventy-year-old body. As he headed to the door he turned and looked upward and said, "Thank you, Laura; I love you."

For the next seventeen years, William took one day at a time praying that his family could remember what had bonded Freemans together for the past 150-plus years, God. Amy had married Percival Johnson in 1918. His boys went off to fight for their country in World War I, both in the army and navy. Eventually, Percival and Amy Johnson, his son William Jr., along with his daughter Bertha Christian all moved to Rochester, New York. Unfortunately, at the time of his death on July 03, 1931, his family had disintegrated into combating components.

His son Horace contrived a bogus will at the time of his death in consort with his brothers Wheeler and Daniel. William's son Wheeler Sr. had abandoned his wife Clara and ten children and moved to Nashville, Tennessee. William's son Daniel went with his brother to Nashville. William's son Claude, who had spent most of his life living with his Uncle Jackson Freeman, found it more advantageous to disassociate himself from his immediate relatives and create a niche for himself in the Fulton, New York, area. Claude took no side in the brewing fiasco.

Horace had taken a "piece of yellow paper" and wrote that the property was his, gifted to him for taking care of his father in his old age. Horace's plot had secured the support of Wheeler Sr. and Daniel. Just prior to his father's death, Horace was able to secure his father's signature on his "scribbled yellow sheet of paper."

On July 03, 1931, the same day William J. Freeman Sr. died, Horace submitted his "scribbled yellow sheet of paper" to the probate office as the "Official Will of William J. Freeman Sr." This bogus will disregarded any rights or wishes for his other children and family members. This caused Amy, Bertha, and William, Jr. to secure attorney Max Goldman to contest Horace's actions and the bogus will he had submitted.

THE CITIZEN ADVERTISER, AUBURN, N.Y., SATURDAY, MARCH 26, 1932

ALLEGED WILL OF FREEMAN, AGED AUBURN NEGRO, REJECTED

Climax Reached in Hard Fought Case When "Wit-

nesses" Appear and Swear They Had Never Before
Seen the Document—Court Denies Probate

This fiasco played out in the courts for two years. Unfortunately, there were people who enjoyed this courtroom circus. They knew that the children were not united in keeping William J. Freeman's assets functional. Without a concerted effort, all of his properties would be forfeited for pennies.

The final anticipated result came to fruition between June 12, 1931 and May 01, 1933. Horace had not paid the taxes on some of the properties, so they were lost in William's waning days. Everything else was lost in May of 1933 to pay outstanding obligations and taxes. All properties that had been owned by the Freemans on Worden Lane, Chapman Ave., Forte St., and Foote St. where the last properties lost.

For decades, the family led a fractured existence with different components, never acknowledging or speaking to other components of the family. Even to the level of components of the family despising other components within the family.

Only God could promote healing and that is what he has done. He began to heal wounds and enter "Forgiveness" into the equations. God is Good!

Over the last ten years we have been rebuilding our family by learning the doctrine of "Forgiveness" or re-membering the doctrine of "Forgiveness." That was what our fore-parents had taught us, "Forgive and Love or Love and Forgive"; that is how you keep God first in your life. That's the rock our Forefathers and Foremothers had adhered to, "Keep God first in everything you do!"

By doing this we found there was no need to play Dr. Frankenstein by trying to create life from the stuff in the "closet of hurt and sorrow." Love is working in our family, and as people grow more in their relationship with their God, the strength to mend, heal, and reunite becomes a reality.

The true dynamic is that the Freeman Family is no different than any other family in the world. We all have to devote our very being to become more "God-Obedient" in our actions and activities during our life. It's a narrow road to travel but is truly the "Road of Reward" for you and me.

God Bless.

CPSIA information can be obtained
at www.ICGtesting.com
Printed in the USA
JSHW010918270222
23386JS00001B/21